It's Only Pain

by
Andy Hopwood

authorHOUSE™

1663 LIBERTY DRIVE, SUITE 200
BLOOMINGTON, INDIANA 47403
(800) 839-8640
WWW.AUTHORHOUSE.COM

First published by AuthorHouse 11/17/05

ISBN: 1-4259-0422-X (sc)

*Printed in the United States of America
Bloomington, Indiana*

This book is printed on acid-free paper.

To my wife Sharon, for being a wonderful person and for giving me the true love, peace, happiness and freedom to make this book possible.

This book is dedicated to the memory of Johan Blomquist and all those who fell.

In loving memory of Thomas and Evelyn Horsley.

Acknowledgements:

Thanks to the extremely thorough Ray Hetherington for suffering editorial duties and for putting up with my inept use of punctuation.

My thanks also go to Adam Bodfish, Richard Smallman, Steve Hart and Marc Garfield for their help and encouragement during the writing process.

Huge appreciation also to Terry Wood, Tony Rowan, Arshid Khaliq, Martin Shaw, Ian Pardoe, Gary Anderson and all at the BFFA for years of dedication and support.

PROLOGUE

(Christmas Eve 1986)

The cold wind blew around my closely cropped head as the flames rose up. I picked up the photograph that had taken pride of place in my Samawian room for the last few years and dropped it in to the fire. The picture had been taken on the day that we had been brought together as the Samawian Special Task Force. I was smiling in the centre of the shot; only a few of the others were still alive.

We had all suffered serious injuries and taken incredible risks in the line of duty and even when we had just been fucking about out drinking, or on one of our climbing and skydiving trips.

I looked back at the faces as the picture blackened with the heat: Freddie and Henry (shit – I had almost forgotten those guys) had been killed on that very first mission at the rebel headquarters.

Benni's cheeky grin was at the side of the picture. The man had suffered a broken heart after his girlfriend's family had died and had run like a man insane with his machine gun blazing, to his certain death before we could stop him.

Sniper fire had taken Juan's life.

Louis, Paul and Jonathan had all perished in the explosion during that catastrophic mission in Cabilo.

Michael, Joseph and Billy were all alive and well two days earlier when I had left them at the base in Moyana, as was Will Boato our commanding officer.

As the cold winter wind blew once more, I reached down to pick up a photograph that had fallen onto the garden path. The picture showed me smiling next to Joe at the summit of Mount Nabinda. We had all had so many laughs and taken so many risks – none of it seemed to make sense any more. Maybe without the mementoes I could start to forget.

CHAPTER ONE

March 1982

"So how am I going to tell Mum & Dad then Gramps?" I asked.

I was sitting with my Grandfather in his back garden, drinking the remnants of a third cup of tea with which my Nan had been plying us. (The typical act of an English grandmother who knows that something untoward is happening, but is not sure whether or not she wants to hear it first hand.)

I was 17 years old, and had the attitude of many a 17 year old lad, probably worse than most.

I don't want you to think that I thought I was invincible. I didn't think that at all – I was fucking certain that I was totally indestructible!

From the age of 6 my parents had been taking me to a minimum of two martial arts classes every week. I had an Uncle who ran a karate school and the husband of a lady that my Mother worked with taught Ju-Jitsu locally. Either my parents didn't want to upset the two instructors, or they saw it as a good excuse to get me out of their hair for a few hours every week. Either way, I grew up studying what I thought at that stage to be a great range of combat systems. After eleven years of training, with school playground and street tests at varying frequencies being successfully dealt with, I had an ego that was growing with incredible vigour.

A day earlier, Steve ("Griff") Griffiths my Ju-Jitsu instructor and I had taken part in a training seminar held in London by a group of Military un-armed combat instructors from Africa who were travelling around the world teaching these sessions. So far they had taught sessions throughout Australia, the U.S.A., Europe; London, Stockholm and Munich.

The training day was unlike anything that I, or any of the participants had ever taken part in before. The instruction was much more informal than any traditional martial arts class and the techniques that were being taught were very simple, explosive and devastatingly effective – yet very easy to learn and remember. I was immediately enthusiastic and trained throughout the day with energy and passion.

At the end of the seminar Will Boato, the Principal Instructor, called me over to discuss the day's training. I explained how excited I was about the techniques that we had been taught during the day. Even with my ego being the size it was, I was pretty astonished when he went on to tell me that he and the rest of the instruction team had been tremendously impressed with my performance. He told me that part of the reason for them touring the world with the training seminars was to search out " talented martial artists" who would be able to fly out to their Head Quarters in Samawi in order to train within the military training school, with the aim of swapping ideas and developing techniques with their instructors. I was even more astounded that he wanted me to fly out within the next 6 weeks for a three-month stay. The first thing I said was the first thing that entered my head, which was something like, "try and fucking stop me!" As I said this, Griff appeared at my side. I explained the situation to the man who, next to my Grandad, did the most to keep me in touch with reality. "You're only 17" he pointed out. For a second or two my heart sunk. That was until Mr Boato pointed out that with parental consent there would be no problem. Which was easy for him to say, he hadn't met my Dad, a man who had never done anything out of the ordinary in his life and who held the opinion that there were two trains of thought in the world: his own and the wrong one! "Count me in! In spite of all that, Gramps will think of something" I told Griff as he looked at me with bewilderment. "What do I need to do to get there Mr. Boato?" I asked smiling at the big African soldier, feeling confident again, "I'll see you in six weeks then!"

So there I was having just explained everything and shown all the paperwork to my Grandad, waiting for him to come up with the ultimate plan in his (what I'd always thought to be) infinite wisdom. After a fourth cup of tea, I was pretty devastated to hear the words: " go tell your parents exactly what you've just told me – see what they say, and if it isn't what you want to hear, come back to me and we'll see what we can do."

"But Gramps!" I started to protest,

"Give them a chance Andy" he interrupted me "I don't think they'll like it anymore than you do, but it's got to be your first step. If they point blank refuse to listen to you, come back to your Nan and me, and we'll see what we can do to help eh?"

Ten o'clock that night I was back at my Grandparent's house. This time drinking the dirty brown liquid that Gramps like to call his "special home brew". My Mother had disappeared into a pile of sobs and tears at my news and my Dad had (rather predictably) refused to listen to anything I had to say and was adamant that there was "no bloody way any son of mine is going to a black mans country – not while I've got any say in the matter!"

So with my father's helpful, constructive and open-minded comments still ringing in my ears, I "hot-tailed" it back to the place I'd always felt most at home.

I knew that my grandparents didn't want me to go any more than my Mum and Dad did . I also knew that they believed firmly in following your heart and if they could help me do that, they would.

Six weeks later – looking back I honestly don't know how – I was sat on a plane flying out to a place I'd never heard of until that incredible day and despite trying to research (to the best of an inexperienced 17 year old's ability) I still didn't know a great deal more about, other than it was an oil rich Republic on the South Atlantic coast which was known to have some civil unrest and sporadic guerrilla warfare. I'd also found out that Samawi had suffered invasion from both Portugal and Britain in its history, so I couldn't claim to be the first European to tread its soil! I was however, incredibly excited, scared out of my mind and extremely anxious (not necessarily in that particular order) and I was definitely going to make the most of the experience!

I descended the steps off the plane at Nabwana airport, the African heat hitting me like a train at full speed. As I stepped on to the asphalt I was met by a man a good six inches shorter than me and I guessed at least a stone lighter (I stood only 5 foot 10" and weighed a very unimpressive 10stone 7lbs at the time – so he was by no means a giant). He was dressed in a pair of jungle camouflage shorts and a blindingly bright orange vest. His head was covered by a khaki baseball cap with what I had recently learnt was the flag of Samawi emblazoned above the peak.

"You are Andrew?" he shouted in my general direction. I guessed that this was a question rather than a statement of a fact and began to answer, but he turned away and walked hurriedly towards what in England would have been considered a battered old lorry with a canvas back. What once was paint was peeling from its body. Looking around at other vehicles in the vicinity, it fitted the surroundings. I guessed that if this guy knew my name, he must be about the only welcome committee that I was going to get, so I followed after him. I wanted to let him know he was doing nothing to improve my already extremely nervous disposition, but somehow I didn't think he'd be too sympathetic!

The small African stood at the back of the truck alternately pointing at me and then the inside of the vehicle. As I reached him, I started to speak but he again turned away from me this time shouting, "we go now – yes!"

"This is some fuckin' welcome," I muttered to myself as I threw my bags into the back of the truck.

A heavily accented voice from inside the hold of the vehicle replied, "I am thinking, like you, this is not a friendly place – yes?"

As the truck's engine fired up, I climbed in behind my luggage to see a young guy, maybe a year or two older than myself. He was tall, built like a brick wall, with a spiky blond haircut, but best of all, he was smiling and his hand was being held out to shake mine. "I am Johan," he told me "it's nice to meet you."

This was quite surreal. We were in this tiny corner of the planet, thousands of miles from (judging by my first impression) either of our homes. Yet, here we were two young men, both of us wearing faded blue jeans, white leather baseball boots and Iron Maiden t-shirts (the Swede's being several sizes bigger than my own)! "Perhaps this crazy adventure is all a dream after all," I thought to myself and then held out my own hand to say instead, "Andy Hopwood." I smiled and said, "I guess you're on the same adventure as I am Johan?"

"Guess so my friend. Call me Joe; you are British yes?" he asked. The truck started on our journey to the further unknown.

"Yeah, from Birmingham, England – you're not local either!" I replied.

"I am a Viking, come to conquer Africa for the glory of Sweden" he stated with a puffed out chest in a manner that led me to believe he wasn't completely joking.

"Judging by our reception so far, the natives aren't too friendly – we may need to become allies for this invasion eh?" I asked. As I spoke, the truck hit a pothole in the road. It was so well timed that I got the impression our diminutive airport greeter could hear every word (which was seriously unlikely over the cacophony from the aging truck's engine.)

The big Swede smacked the back of his head on one of the steel uprights that were holding the tarpaulin back on. He mumbled something that I took to be Scandinavian obscenities. I wasn't any more comfortable than the Swede, it was incredibly hot, our shirts were wet with sweat and I began to wish I'd listened to my Nan about getting my hair cut, as it was half way down my back and sticking to my face and anything else it came into contact with in the 'mobile sauna'.

Our bizarre journey continued in the same vein for what seemed to be many hours but in reality was more like forty-five minutes. In this time Johan and I had been trying our very best to hold a conversation, hindered by the deafening engine and the unfortunate state of the roads. I had however decided that my newfound friend could curse and blaspheme in a manner that out matched even my foul mouth. I had also discovered that we shared a passion for rock climbing and an obsession with British rock music (his father had been a music journalist for a magazine in Stockholm) along with making immature, pig-headed and downright foolish decisions that involve travelling fantastic distances to obscure countries in the name of expanding our martial arts skills.

During the trip, I was taken aback by the scenery, I had no real idea about what to expect, but the lush green hills and fields of cane undulating down to the shores of the Atlantic took me by surprise.

We eventually drove past some high wire fencing topped with razor wire and the truck stopped abruptly in what was obviously a military camp. My new found Viking friend and I swore in unison and looked at each other with nervous anticipation before gratefully climbing out of the world's least comfortable truck.

Our diminutive escort was speedily walking towards the nearest of what looked to be a mass of concrete buildings, again gesturing to us to follow him. The big Swede shrugged at me and we duly tagged along behind the little African.

He led us through a veritable rabbit warren of corridors and dormitories, at last coming to a halt at a side room with a large barred window and two bunks. On the opposite wall were a couple of shoddily put together wardrobes and another door. "This is where you live!" the small man exclaimed, but at least his face cracked into a smile as he did so, "you need anything, ask for William, no problem!" and with that, he was gone again.

"So he is called William eh?" Johan laughed.

"Fucking Billy Whizz! The man's like lightning," I said, walking towards the

door that I'd spotted on the other side of the room. "Looks like we'll be sharing with a few others," I called back to Johan, not realizing he was right there at my shoulder. The door led to a tiled room which consisted of a urinal, two sinks with mirrors and two frontless shower cubicles with a hole in the floor of each, which we later discovered was to assist with "lengthier toilet visits!" Walls were dotted with small, light green lizards and the floor seemed to be a popular venue with the local insect community.

"Home sweet farken home eh?" Johan laughed as he punched my shoulder with a bit more force than I thought was necessary, but I let it pass.

"I need to talk to you about that my friend," I smiled at the big man, "that's going to grate with me unless we sort it out – it's 'fucking', not 'farken' – you need to work on it if we're going to be living together Joe my mate!" Without looking in his direction, I threw my bags into the better of the two wardrobes, and quickly climbed onto the top bunk. I then turned to give the Swede my best friendly Cheshire cat style grin.

"You are a farken bastard I think," He was shaking his head, walking towards me, he put his face just a bit too close for comfort to my own, "but we will get along like brothers – yes?" He punched me, this time on top of the head, with just a little too much force again.

I couldn't help but like him, "yeah – like brothers" I agreed.

I unpacked the few things I'd brought from England and put them all in any place that I thought might have the remotest chance of being safe from insect invasion. I asked my new room mate if he fancied having a look around what was going to be our home for the next few months.

Stepping back outdoors, the heat was like nothing I'd ever experienced before. Gramps had told me that the sun was a ruthless bastard in Africa and as the sweat streamed out of every pore, I made a mental note to listen to him with even more diligence if I should make it back to Birmingham without melting.

We walked across the asphalted area where Billy Whizz had parked the truck, and turned the corner heading behind what appeared to be the main building. There was an assault course beyond an area of gravelled ground on which were parked maybe a dozen open-backed Land Rovers, about half of which were fitted with a large machine gun above the cab. Three soldiers walked towards us, all smoking, all armed with machine guns and all gesturing towards Johan and myself, laughing and obviously joking about us. They kept this going until they were very close, when the joking suddenly stopped but they didn't. I managed to move in time, but Johan was hit with a shoulder to the sternum and forced into a wall. The three soldiers kept walking; there was no change of pace at all. I called them a few not too complimentary names, but having seen their guns up close, I thought I'd leave it at that for the time being. They were laughing again and I turned my attention to seeing if the Swede was ok. He was.

We explored the grounds for an hour or so without further interruption other than a few inquisitive looks from distance. We discovered a large pond surrounded by fruit trees. It seemed like an oasis of natural beauty in a soldier's world and there was a trail leading over white sand dunes to a beach in a small bay surrounded by cliffs. It looked like the kind of place the average person only sees in the movies where the hero is shipwrecked and accidentally discovers paradise.

"This will do." I said. Johan turned to look at me, I put my hand on his shoulder and pointed at the beach and the sea beyond, telling him, " if everything else here turns out to be hell my friend, this will fucking do for me!"

CHAPTER TWO

I woke from a sleep that had been, at best, fitful. The sound of small scurrying feet (along with the incessant scratching and clicking of the innumerable insects, lizards and fuck knows what else that shared our rooms) did nothing to aid a peaceful nights sleep despite the tiring journey and excitement of the previous day.

Johan was already up and in the shower singing "My Generation" by The Who loudly to himself in perfect Roger Daltrey English. I got myself cleaned up and dressed too. That done, we were discussing how to go about discovering where to eat breakfast, apart from Billy Whizz and the antagonistic soldiers we had, quite literally, bumped into, we had seen nobody at all to talk to since our extremely low key arrival. As we came to a decision to visit the fruit trees that we'd discovered and harvest our own breakfast, the door to our room opened and I recognized Joseph, one of the instructors from the seminar in London. I made a mental note to lock the door overnight from that day forward as Joseph spoke, "good morning, how do you like Samawi so far?" Before either of us could answer he swiftly followed his rhetorical question with, "you come with me please!" and turned to rapidly disappear down the corridor. Johan looked at me in disbelief, I shrugged. "Must be a local custom or something, I'm just glad we were dressed mate." I said, and with that we hurried after him.

We arrived in a large dining hall, the kind you get in High Schools. Joseph directed us to a table in a corner at the far end of the hall. Already sat at the table were six people: Will Boato, the Chief Instructor who'd invited me to make this trip; Billy Whizz; two of the none too friendly soldiers from the previous day and, to my surprise, two more white guys looking about as anxious as I was now feeling.

At Will's request we joined them all at the table and were introduced to everybody we hadn't already met. The two soldiers were PT Instructors at the camp, their names were given as Michael and Peter (they'd already demonstrated that they were no Saints). Peter stared at Johan for the duration of the introductions without uttering a word. The two white men were an American from Dallas (who told us to call him J.J.) He had the appearance of an 'All American' college football star, short cropped hair cut in the "U.S. Marines" style and a film star set of teeth. My Nan had often told me not to go on first impressions, but I took an instant dislike to J.J.

The final member of this peculiar breakfast party was Gerd, a German from Hamburg. "Like Gerd Muller?" I asked as he told us his name. "Exactly so!" He replied with pride at the mention of the famous German footballer.

After the introductions were done, Will, Joseph and Peter left. William (Billy Whizz) and Michael led us across the hall to a buffet style layout of meats, fish, breads and fruits. J.J., Gerd, Johan and I ate with the appetite of people who hadn't eaten with the regularity they were used to and weren't sure when they'd eat next. Before he'd left, Will Boato had explained that we would be meeting for a combat training session in two hours, so we were probably all trying to put some energy in to our bodies too.

Over breakfast, I had discovered that William was actually an extremely likeable man. He had been in the army since returning to Samawi at the age of nineteen after dropping out of college in Cape Town, where his uncle was a Dentist. Johan decided to let him know that we called him Billy Whizz behind his back. He did not mind at all. In fact, he seemed quite pleased with the nickname. Michael had joined in the conversation too, he had a cousin living in Wolverhampton, no more than twenty miles from my own home. He was more than a little disappointed to discover that I didn't know his cousin personally!

J.J. was incredibly loud, butting in and generally being arrogant at every opportunity, he wanted everybody to know how he had won every martial arts tournament that he'd ever entered from the age of eight (he was currently twenty four years old) and that he was the tae kwon do champion of Texas. Gerd sat quietly through most of the meal, only speaking when asked a direct question, or if he felt there was something relevant to say. His father was a Karate instructor with a full time gym in Hamburg and Gerd it seemed was living to his Dad's wishes. I decided that he was a nice guy, but I didn't think he was a particularly strong character. By the end of the breakfast gathering I was starting to feel slightly more comfortable with my new surroundings and

I had begun to look forward to the first combat training session.

Two and a half hours later, my mindset had changed completely again!

I was lying in a hospital bed after taking a beating of the like nobody should have to endure. As far as I was aware the "combat training session" was still going on. I had been the first of the 'guests' up to take part in the training. Will Boato had gathered about thirty of us, all resident soldiers apart from Johan, Gerd, J.J., and myself, we all sat around the outskirts of the matted area in the huge sports hall, I was totally comfortable with the environment at this stage, as it felt just like any sparring session in any Martial Arts Dojo that I'd been in since I could walk without wobbling. Will announced that in the morning's session we would be looking at how it felt to be in a hand to hand combat situation when it really mattered, when your life is at stake, when it is either you or your opponent that walks away, no other choice available – it is them or you! I sat there listening to him, feeling totally psyched. I had absolute belief in my ability and I couldn't wait for the chance to fight someone, anyone; I had never been so wrong.

My over confidence must have been like a beacon to Will.

"So we begin with the combat!" He announced. He then pointed at a soldier who appeared to be about my size and weight sat next to Billy Whizz on the opposite side of the mats to me and the other guests and said, "you. And Andy I think," pointing at me. I couldn't wait for this opportunity to show off my skills, every fight I'd ever been in had been no real problem for me. I nudged Johan as I stood up to walk on to the mats, "I won't be long Joe, my man – keep my place for me!"

Facing the soldier in the centre of the mats, I realized he was a lot older than I was, (closer to my Dad's age). My confidence grew even more; I could embarrass this old guy and show everybody just how good I was.

I adopted my classic fighting stance in the way I had done since the age of six: hands up in a 'guard' and feet separated to give balance, with a low centre of gravity. The soldier stood looking at me in a casual standing position. I gave him my best competition 'psyche out' stare, he smiled back at me.

"Fight" shouted Will.

I swear I never had the chance to move, let alone hit the guy. He came at me like the proverbial speeding train. I remember a low kick that caught me hard on the right knee. As I dropped slightly because of it, an elbow caught me full in the face and I felt my nose explode. It could have stopped there, but it didn't, not for a split second. The blows kept coming with full force despite the fact that I hadn't even started to throw a single strike. I had never known anything like this, I was crying, literally, and my face was pissing with blood, not just from my nose. He'd hammered me with so many shots to the face and head that there were several cuts in that area. I staggered, desperately trying to regain my balance; he was hitting me with everything he'd got. I hadn't got a clue where the next shot was coming from. If it wasn't going to be stopped I knew I had to do something.

I began to throw a punch; he easily dodged it and caught me hard in the lower back as I started to fall. I hit the ground and I felt my bladder give way as the beating continued. I gave up. I lay on the ground curled in a ball desperately trying to protect myself from the onslaught, desperately wanting this to end, covered in my own blood and piss. The blows kept coming, I laid still as I began to feel the incredible searing pain from my wounds as my opponent created even more. I started to cry and beg him to stop as my bowels opened and my humbling was complete.

So, I lay there in the Military Hospital bed, the agony from my physical wounds was incredible. It paled into insignificance by the devastation that my ego had suffered. I had always believed that I couldn't lose. Everybody that I had ever trained with knew it and whether they liked it or not believed that too. From the age of six I'd entered just about every competition that I could enter and won them all. I was faster than everyone and better than anyone – that's what I had always believed. But, not only had I lost, I had been totally fucking annihilated - physically and emotionally.

By the time I had healed, my train of thought had changed beyond all recognition.

All the training that I'd ever taken part in, all the tuition from Griff (who I had total respect for and loved dearly) and every other martial arts instructor that I had studied under, had all been totally worthless when it comes down to fighting for your life. I had thought that I'd been in 'real' fights before.

They had all been nothing more than scuffles. The truth dawned on me as I endured the slow process of healing.

What I had, was good basic fighting skills. That meant absolutely "jack shit" without the correct preparation, experience and mental tenacity to put it into practice when it really matters!

(Will Boato was to tell me some years later that this had been his intention all along.)

Walking along the white sand of the beach ten days later, I shared my thoughts with Johan. The big Swede had been to see me each day since that 'training session', sometimes on his own, occasionally with Gerd (J.J. had been too wrapped up in his own woes). All of us had taken a severe beating on that day, all from different soldiers. Johan had told me that he and Gerd thought that mine had been the worst as I was first, and after seeing the hammering I had taken, the others had yielded with a bit more haste. Yet he still had more than his fair share of facial cuts and bruises from the fight when he first visited me in hospital. Johan had agreed with my conclusions regarding the lesson learnt from taking the pounding in that first taste of African combat. We made a pact to stay to learn all that the soldiers had learnt, share the necessary combat experiences and do whatever it took for as long as it took, to become the best we could possibly be.

From that day forward (still a little sorely at first) I was up with the African lark (always accompanied by a foul mouthed modern day Viking) running across the camp in the early, yet still hot, morning sun. We ran down to and along the beach to start our days training. We'd practice traditional Karate techniques at the water's edge for a minimum of thirty minutes before running back to the fruit trees by the pool back on the camp and eating a fresh fruit breakfast with some breads supplied by Billy Whizz (whose wife worked in the kitchens). The beauty of the ancient techniques fascinated him and he even took to joining us on the two days a month he was allowed to take off from his army duties.

We trained like men possessed for the remainder of our designated three month stay. After breakfast we would stay in the training hall for the whole day working on all aspects of unarmed combat. If there was a training session taking place we would join in, if not we just pushed each other to the limit at whatever exercise we hadn't practiced for a day or two. Everything we needed was there; there was no need to go elsewhere, other than to eat or the occasional call of nature! At first, it seemed that we were the butt of the camp jokes. But, after everyone noticed the progress we were making, we seemed to gain their respect, slowly but surely.

One week to the day before we were due to go home, Will Boato appeared amongst the fruit trees as we were picking fresh figs after our morning beach run. He told us how impressed he'd been with our reaction to the "different way they do things" and asked if we would extend our stay indefinitely. I had no hesitation in accepting the invitation, I had become totally obsessed with my quest to gain all the combat experience that Samawi had to offer; I also had very little to go home for. Johan on the other hand took a little longer to decide, he came from a very happy family home. He called his parents to talk it over before agreeing to prolong his stay too.

That night, I was sitting on the ground, talking under the fruit trees by the pool, with Billy (Whizz), Gerd, Johan, Michael, Peter and Joseph (who having been training with us most days had become a friend). Gerd had been telling us how he would be going home the following Saturday when

J.J. turned up. Without saying a word to anyone he headed straight for me.

I heard Gerd start to say, "hey J.J. where have you been...?"

Everybody remained seated. When J.J. got within striking distance of my face he aimed a kick straight at it, I managed to dodge the boot and roll in to an upright position. I decided not to ask him what his fucking problem was and instead launched into an attack of the same brutality that I had recently endured on that first training day! The American fell after I landed a hard-driven kick to the side of his knee. I kept hitting him and would probably have continued to do so, but Johan, Gerd and Billy dragged me away, while Joseph and Michael got J.J. to his feet.

"Motherfucker!" I heard the scream behind me and turned to see the American coming towards me with a knife aimed at my chest. There was no time for thought, I simply reacted and, before I knew it, J.J. was back on the floor, screaming more obscenities and holding the knife again, but this time it was buried to the hilt in his thigh!

Talking the night's events through with everybody else the next day, it seemed that J.J. had not been asked to stay on and was most pissed off because Johan and I had. We deduced that he picked on me, probably because I was smaller than him (not built like a Swedish brick wall) and that he'd grabbed the knife from the sheath on Michael's belt. He had since been patched up and was being held in solitary until they could get him on the next flight back to the U.S. I was not sorry for anything that had happened, I had never liked J.J. I still don't know exactly how I came to take the knife off him, or what made me stick it in his leg rather than somewhere more permanently damaging, but I guess I'm glad I did. He was and probably always will be an asshole, but he didn't deserve to die that night!

Over the following weeks and months, the training hall more and more became the domain of Johan and myself. Michael, Joseph and Billy continued to be regular Instructors, and Will Boato would make his presence felt as often as he could, but he was in charge of a large base and therefore an extremely busy man. The daily training that took place in the hall was still, at this stage, mostly conducted by the African instructors, but we found ourselves getting more and more involved with the instruction and I no longer felt isolated. This trait continued to develop, so much so that by the time Christmas came (just nine months after first arriving in the country) I found myself having to go back to England knowing that I had to explain to my parents and loved ones that I had been offered a full time position at the base as an unarmed combat instructor. I also had to explain that I had decided to accept the job and stay on indefinitely!

CHAPTER THREE

(January 1983)

It had gone about as well as I'd expected it to go with my family. Mum had cried, Dad had shouted, and my sisters had sided with my parents – all true to form!

Gramps had been upset at the prospect of not seeing much of his only grandson, but as usual, was totally supportive and understanding. Nan was obviously not happy either, but as always, made lots of tea and backed Gramps one hundred per cent.

Now, here I was, back in Nabwana Airport, hot and hung-over, having just got off the plane. I'd realized that I had no reason to stay in Birmingham. My parents had driven me crazy trying to change my mind at every opportunity, most of my old friends had been busy with their own family festivities or out with new girlfriends. I had visited Griff the day before and let him know my plans. He was as supportive as he'd always been and as I slumped in an armchair at his house, sharing vast amounts of beer and wine, he and his lovely wife Jenny announced that they were expecting their first child in the coming Spring – so we drank more alcohol in celebration.

Walking through the airport grounds (my hangover now diminishing) I was looking around for a taxi, when one found me – braking hard, less than half a metre from my feet . A spiky blond head appeared out of the window "don't just farken stand there Andy my man, throw your bags in the back and let's farken go!"

During the cab journey back to our Samawian base in Moyana on the coast, I tried to teach Johan how to swear properly in English while he explained to me that he'd initially had the same sort of response from his family at the news of his offer of employment (which was the same as my own). However, his parents were obviously more open minded than mine, as they'd mellowed over the holiday period and before his return journey they'd given him their full support and approval.

Walking back into my room (Johan and I had been issued single rooms in a new building at the base a few months earlier) I realized that I had actually missed the place. I hastily unpacked, showered, dressed in something cooler and went down to the training hall, only to find Michael and Billy sat in the middle of the matted area. We immediately began talking and catching up; it felt like I really belonged in this place.

Maybe twenty minutes had gone by when Joseph walked in to the hall with a man that I immediately recognized. The man that had given me that beating in that dreadful first combat session all those months before, Joseph was his usual smiling, friendly self, but the other man was staring straight at me. He too was smiling, but his smile did not reach his eyes. I stood up with the intention of shaking his hand; there was no way this man was going to intimidate me. He had made a good job of beating me up on that first day, but not through superior skill or knowledge, he'd taken me by surprise and he had the necessary brutality to keep hitting me even though I was not fighting back. I had come along way since then.

I held out my hand to the man as he came towards me, he took it, gripping hard as he spat in my face. Without any thought I brought my other arm across and smashed my elbow hard into his face feeling his nose crumble under the impact. I kept hitting and kicking with the same relentless ferocity that this man had used against me. I had no thoughts of compassion; I was not fighting to any rules. This man had tried to intimidate, ridicule and embarrass me, but he had made the mistake of thinking that I was still the same person that had stood in front of him before. He was to learn the hard way.

The still figure lay on the floor at my feet. I had eventually stopped kicking him. Joseph, Billy and Michael stood looking at me with mouths open. Even these experienced and ruthless fighting men were taken aback at the vicious counter-attack I had aimed at their colleague. None of them had moved to pull me away from him. The volley of strikes had probably not lasted more than a matter of seconds, but I was exhausted physically and mentally. Nausea hit me. I rushed in to the shower room and vomited forcefully until there was nothing left in me.

I walked back in to the training hall to find Billy mopping vigorously where the man had fallen. Michael, Joseph and the spitting man were nowhere to be seen.

Billy explained that the man, who's name was Isaac, was a member of an elite (but apparently not too popular) army unit based at the camp, he and the rest of the soldiers in that group had recently arrived back after a mission elsewhere in the country. Isaac, it seemed, was not exactly renowned for being Mr Friendly, but he did have a reputation as the Samawian army's top bully. Two things rapidly became very apparent to me, 1. This was going to be a very hot story with the camp gossipmongers and 2. My scalp was going to be extremely sought after by Isaac and his mates for the foreseeable future.

I wondered if they had any more missions coming up that might take them away again.

Michael, Joseph and an excitable Viking entered the hall disturbing my already disturbed thoughts. "What the fark have you been doing Andy?" asked Johan as he hurried towards me, " they say that this guy is half farken dead – I turn my back on you for just a few minutes man, I didn't expect you to start eliminating the locals!"

I explained what exactly had happened and also what Billy had told me about Isaac and his unit. Johan didn't seem overly concerned at the news (but then it wasn't his ass on the line.) "We'll handle it Andy, don't farken worry, if we stick together, we'll have no problems eh?" He tried to assure me.

"Thanks Joe my man," I told him, " but to be honest, I wouldn't be too anxious about fighting any of the fuckers in a fist fight any more, but in case it's passed you by, my big Viking brother, these bastard's all carry guns!"

"Let's go see the beach eh?" he said smiling, "you can't have seen the ocean in a month – not in farken Birmingham – and everything always seems better by the ocean eh?"

Billy had finished cleaning up, Michael and Joseph stood looking in our direction with two bottles of the local 90% proof fire water in their hands and supportive smiles on their faces. Suddenly, I felt very close to this group of relatively new friends. Looking at them then, I knew that I would be able to count on any one of them for back up at any time should I need it.

We all locked up the hall and went down to the beach together. After a few weeks away from the place it struck me again just how beautiful the bay was. We lit a larger than necessary campfire and all drank ourselves into an incredibly drunken stupor.

At dawn the following morning, I was woken by seawater pouring on my face; it was Johan. We were still on the beach, where we'd fallen asleep. The others had all gone off to their relative duties and I was left alone with the Swedish slapstick comedian.

"Joe you f…" I began to shout, and quickly stopped myself as the pain in my head reminded me of the evil liquid I'd consumed just hours before.

We got ourselves together and walked back up to the camp. As we returned to our rooms, I found a young soldier standing outside my door. He had a message asking me to go immediately to Will Boato's office.

Will was sat behind his large, polished mahogany desk with a stern look on his face. I felt like I had felt too many times at school when summoned to the Head Master's office. He asked me to sit down (which, given the state of my poor pounding head, I was quite relieved about) and went on to explain that Isaac had been treated in the military hospital. Along with the nose damage that I was already aware of, he had a fractured cheekbone, three broken ribs, a dislocated shoulder and had undergone surgery for internal bleeding. I didn't know what to say, I was not about to apologise (I wasn't sorry) but I was very aware that Isaac was one of Will's soldiers and I was a mere guest.

I looked in to the big Officer's eyes, hoping to find an indication of his opinion on this matter. He held my gaze for what seemed like a very long time, before speaking again, "I have had reports from the three witnesses to the fight, they all say exactly the same thing – that you were provoked – in fact two of them have stated that in their opinions, you should have killed the bastard!" he grinned broadly before adding, "and I must say Andy, having been his Commanding Officer for too many years, I probably agree with them!" I slumped in to the chair with both relief and disbelief (it was never like this with the Head Master.)

"The soldier will be dealt with accordingly. You almost certainly will not see him again." Will continued. I was stunned. I sat looking at him unable to take in what I was hearing.

"Go on, you're needed in the Training Hall – but get yourself cleaned up first!" He said.

I couldn't get out of there quickly enough; I felt as though if I stayed any longer he would change his mind and send me back to England or stick me in a military prison. Either way the man had seemed almost pleased at the punishment I'd dished out to Isaac and all I wanted to do now was to get on with my new job. I hurried back to my room, had a rapid shit, shower and shampoo (Gramps had always referred to these as "the three S's") and raced up to the Training Hall in time to find Michael explaining the day's program to Johan. On asking if Michael was going somewhere else, I was astonished to find out that Will Boato had ordered that he and Joseph were to oversee and monitor the following months training. He had plans for the vast majority of unarmed combat training to be led by Johan and me! This was totally off the fucking wall, I was just eighteen years old, (Johan was only twenty) less than ten months had gone by since arriving in Africa, I'd just been let off with an attempted murder (at least that's probably what it would have been seen as in the U.K.) and now I find out that I'm soon going to be jointly running the day to day instruction of the Army's unarmed combat school. At least with all the excitement my hangover had gone.

I looked at Joe; he appeared to be as taken aback as I was. For once he appeared to be speechless. All I could think of to say was "OK let's get on with it then!"

The next few weeks flew by like lightning. We trained harder than ever, up every morning with the dawn (most days this required me to virtually kick the big Swede's door down). We ran to the beach to train before breakfasting on freshly picked fruit and warm bread supplied by Billy's wife Paula, before putting a seemingly endless stream of soldiers through the varying training routines.

We both taught with a genuine enthusiasm, always getting physically involved in the instruction, demonstrations and testing of the techniques. The feedback from the participants was fantastic and the reaction from Will Boato reflected this fact. "I want you to look at developing the training program further," he told us after the end of the first month, "it is essential that you incorporate some of the skills and technical knowledge from your Martial Arts backgrounds into what we've been doing already, and also that the army put you guys through some pretty severe military training. What do you think?"

"Farken excellent!" exclaimed Joe

"No problem!" I agreed with a grin. This was basically what we'd spent every morning since the New Year doing on the beach – we'd already developed what we thought were some great techniques, it would be good to expand upon these and build on our knowledge.

So over the following months the Training Hall grew to be known as the realm of the Englishman and the Viking. Will Boato spent at least two days per week with us working on the development of the simple yet at the same time remarkable new techniques. He seemed as excited as we were with the whole new combat system that was forming as we worked together. The guy was an awesome athlete and an incredibly skilled fighter. Between the group of us (including Michael, Joseph and Billy) the Army's unarmed combat training program was transformed and improved dramatically. Johan and I gained an increasing reputation for training hard, testing everybody to their personal limits but teaching devastatingly effective methods of fighting.

We also had become notorious for being inseparable; we had indeed become "like brothers" as Joe had once suggested we would.

Even on our days off we would be together, visiting the bars and markets of Nabwana, climbing on the cliffs around the bay. We even talked some of the camp's parachute instructors into teaching us how to sky dive, which soon became a weekly ritual. However, the big Swede did disappear on his own one weekend; nobody knew where he'd gone. It was the rare occurrence of a long weekend break for us; four full days of leisure. I had arranged with Michael and Billy to spend the Friday climbing before going into Nabwana for a night out drinking in the bars and clubs that they knew (it was always a better night out with their local knowledge and expertise). We had searched for Johan on the Friday morning to get him to come with us, but to no avail. The Friday had gone to plan, we had climbed a couple of previously unconquered routes on the cliffs before going in to the Capitol and crashing in to a party that a cousin of Michaels was hosting and we all got blindsided by that terrible local brew again. I spent the Saturday hanging around on the beach with Billy, Paula and their eight year old son. I was nursing another horrendous hangover and needed the recovery time.

On the Sunday, I went on a sky diving trip over the Great Nomali River, which flows through Samawi from the massive Mount Nabinda in the north to the Southern Atlantic coast. It was with Michael, Billy, Joseph, Will Boato and a group of Para's who took us across the country in a large aging army helicopter. This was my first ever helicopter flight which was exhilarating enough, but the scenery as we flew across Samawi was breathtaking. The jump itself out onto the terrain of the Nomali was simply spectacular; so much so, that we decided to set up camp and do it all again on the Monday morning before flying back to base.

We arrived back at base late on the Monday afternoon. I was still buzzing with the thrill and adrenaline of the trip. I took myself off to my room for the usual "three S's" and to catch up on my sleep, having spent the previous night without a sleeping bag, let alone a tent, on the banks of the Nomali. No matter how much my colleagues assured me there were no crocodiles in that part of the river, I only slept briefly and restlessly.

I had just put my head down, when I heard a crashing sound against my door; I jumped out of bed and rushed to open up. Joe was slumped in the corridor looking like shit; he definitely didn't appear to have been enjoying his weekend break.

After helping him into his room and manoeuvring him under the shower (still fully clothed) to clean and wake him up a bit, I found out what the Viking warrior had been up to for the previous three days.

It turned out that, on our last trip to Nabwana's bars, Joe had arranged to meet a pretty young waitress called Georgia on his next leave. So, having borrowed an army Land Rover, he'd met up with her early on Friday morning and they set off on a trip along Samawi's coastline. They had travelled as far south as Calo, seeing beautiful views over the South Atlantic shores sleeping in the back of the Land Rover and apparently having "farken incredible sex!"

Things had gone wonderfully well until the Monday morning when they pulled up outside the door of the bar (which Georgia's parents owned) to find her Father, three brothers and a couple of other male relatives waiting for them. It soon become obvious that Georgia hadn't been completely honest with her family about her plans for the weekend and that she had taken off without letting anybody know her whereabouts. She had however, told a female cousin in a fit of girly excitement, which is how her Dad had known roughly when Georgia and Joe would be arriving back! The decidedly pissed off relatives got even more irate when the big Swede had got out of the Land Rover to try and make a joke out of the situation. They had attacked him – he couldn't tell me exactly how he'd got away, just pure panic and strength through fear seemed to have got him back into the vehicle and back to the camp, where he finally slumped against the door to my room!

We got him checked over by the medics, but apart from a bruised ego (and a previously favourite bar which now had to be avoided) there was no real damage.

CHAPTER FOUR

I was lost – not a fucking clue where I was – I suppose the only thing I did know was that I was still in Samawi, but that was about the limit of my wisdom as far as my location was concerned.

Six of us had been loaded in to the hold of an army wagon, our pockets emptied (we were allowed a standard issue combat knife) and then blindfolded.

We were to be driven to varying points in Samawi, dropped off individually and left to make our own way back to base; apparently this was a test of inner strength, resourcefulness, endurance and tenacity. The most unbelievable thing about the fact that I was in this God-forsaken predicament however, was that I'd actually volunteered for it!

"It could be worse," I thought to myself as I started to walk (to where I didn't know), "if this was at home it would be pissing down with rain!"

After roughly an hours walk, all down hill away from mountains and towards the ocean in the distance, I saw a small settlement. Hoping that the natives would be friendly,

I picked up the pace and headed towards it. I hadn't got too far when I heard a shout away to my right, a young boy of about ten years old was stood with a herd of goats. He was waving in my direction and coming towards me. I stopped and waited for him to reach me. As he got to within a few yards he shouted again, "hey Mr Tourist, I see your brother, I take you to him – yes?"

I had no idea what the boy was talking about, I had no real brother and if I did surely he wouldn't be stupid enough to put himself in the ludicrous situations I seemed to get into (Joe was back at base so it wasn't him either). There was also the fact that I wasn't exactly a tourist (I was even dressed in army issue camouflage combat uniform). The lad was smiling and he seemed friendly and eager to help, so I let him clarify his initial statement.

"I see a white man and his lady travel here yesterday on big motorbike – I told him stay with my Uncle in Logato – I take you to him, yes? He is your brother I think," he stood about as tall as my chest and seemed to have a permanent smile.

"How far is Logato?" I asked him

"One hour's walk. I show you your brother?" he replied, "come – this way!"

So, after an hour's walk down hills covered with maize fields in which numerous women toiled as their offspring played, the ocean in view for the duration of our journey, we arrived at a town with streets decorated on either side with mango and fig trees and houses of Portuguese architecture. As we turned a corner the boy stopped and pointed towards a large white building that had obviously once been a mansion but was now a hotel. A large unshaven Samawian came out

33

of the front doors of the building and, on seeing us, walked quickly in our direction. The boy ran towards him shouting remarks about 'finding another one!'

Shaking my hand, the man introduced himself in perfect English as Fernando, the manager of the hotel and as he led us into the building he explained that his nephew had happened to meet a Dutch couple who were travelling through Africa on a Harley Davison motorbike. They were indeed staying at his hotel while the bike had some much needed repairs done at a local garage. As we entered the lobby he gestured towards a bar, at which sat two very disconsolate looking European people.

The big manager gestured for me to move closer to him and whispered

"Please. They have problems with their journey, they very unhappy – maybe they be happy to see you – I think so."

I shrugged and wandered in to the bar to introduce myself, more out of curiosity than anything else as I still had problems of my own. I knew that I was in Logato, but I hadn't a fucking clue where that was, or how far away from Moyana and the base I was.

The couple told me that their names were Marc and Suzi; they were from Rotterdam. I guessed that they were both in their forties. They explained that Marc was a Lawyer and Suzi a Doctor, and that they had taken a year off to travel through Africa while they were still young and fit enough as it was something that they'd always dreamed of doing. The problem was that they had got this far without too many problems (other than the bike having a few blow outs and the engine needing a bit of 'professional adjustment'), but the officials in Samawi didn't seem as willing as most to help the intrepid travellers. Marc was concerned about getting the necessary papers and stamps to allow them to make their way through the rest of Africa to complete their journey.

As the conversation continued, I explained how circumstances had led me to cross their path. It happened that the next stop on their travels was going to be Nabwana. They planned to travel on to Gabale in the North of Samawi to gain entry into the neighbouring Republic of Cobolo, where Suzi had a contact working at a plantation. Looking at the route on Marc's map, I suggested that I might ask Will Boato for some advice and help when I got back. Fernando had joined us again and informed me that, if I needed transport, there was a bus leaving from the end of the road bound for Nabwana in the morning. I laughed cynically at how ridiculously easily my predicament could be solved if I had the required bus fare. My amusement however, led Suzi to suggest that they give me the necessary fee and that I repay them when they travel to meet me at the base in a few days (after the bike was back in full working order) to see if Will was indeed able to help them. I couldn't believe my luck. I felt almost as though I was cheating, the exercise was surely meant to be putting me through some danger and adversity, not just a long walk downhill, a chance meeting with a Dutchman and his wife and a bus ride on credit! But, not wishing to look the proverbial gift horse in the mouth, I accepted her kind offer and the following morning (after sleeping under a tree in the hotel gardens) I duly joined the swarm of people waiting for the Nabwana bus. It was obvious straightaway that there was no structured queuing system at this unorthodox bus stop; it was a definite 'first come first served' affair.

There were all kinds of people in the throng (and far too many for just the one bus). There were women with young children, men in suits (mostly ill-fitting,) elderly ladies, groups of excitable school kids and a large scar-faced man in traditional African dress who seemed to be continually staring in my direction. I reassured myself that he probably meant no malice and that he was more than likely wondering what the hell a young white man was doing waiting for a bus in Logato! I got on with developing my plan of how to ensure my place as a passenger when the means of transportation arrived. At the edge of the waiting crowd, a young mother was struggling to control her two highly strung sons. I guessed that they were only aged around seven or eight years old but they were causing their Mum a great deal of stress. However, it had reminded me of a trick I had often used with my mates back home when we needed to get through the multitudes of fans at rock festivals.

The bus finally pulled up and I made my move; I leapt forwards sweeping up one of the young Mum's boys and signalling for her to follow. I ran towards the doors of the vehicle shouting, "Step back, this child is sick! Please let us through, this boy is sick!"

The boy's mother at first began to protest, but as she saw the people reluctantly parting to let us through, she quickly picked up on the fact that she would be getting a seat and joined in with my pretence. Sure enough within a few minutes, the bus was full and more than half of the mob that had been waiting was left behind as we pulled away. I felt quite smug, my plan had worked; I was seated in an aisle seat towards the back of the bus. The young mother and her unruly sons were on the back seat annoying the hell out of three shabbily suited men who were sharing that position (Mum and the boy that I'd grabbed often glancing in my direction, obviously thinking that I was quite insane). All the seats were full and to my surprise only a handful of people had been allowed to stand. They were all towards the front of the bus and appeared to be taking it in turns to have a rant at the driver. Apart from that group (and the two brats at the back) all appeared calm. Three seats in front of me, the big traditionally dressed man (complete with facial scars) had also gained passage, and still seemed to be staring at me; I still let it pass.

The journey continued in the same manner for an hour or so. The standing handful were ranting intermittently at the driver (usually after a pot hole or poor piece of road surfacing). The unruly kids began to settle or were running out of energy and everybody else seemed settled already, I began to feel more relaxed too. I adjusted my position in my seat in an attempt to make myself more comfortable. As I did this all hell seemed to be let loose; the scar faced man jumped out of his seat pulling a machete from inside his cloak and, raising it above his head, aimed it towards me. As his arm came down, I half stood and managed to block it. He was screaming fanatically as he brought the big blade down again. Standing now, I blocked again and hit him hard in the chest with my other hand, driving him back towards the front of the bus.

As one, the other passengers became totally inanimate and looked anywhere but at the ongoing struggle for my life!

Realising that something out of the ordinary was happening on his vehicle, the driver jumped on the brakes as the machete came towards me once more. Again I managed to block the scarred man's insane attack and strike him hard in the sternum. The blow to his chest coupled with the bus suddenly stopping sent him off balance. Falling backwards he still managed to swing another crazed blow towards me with the machete. I was moving towards him and only managed to half block this time and I felt the blade slice at my neck as I put my whole body weight behind an elbow, striking at the side of the madman's head. He slumped and fell badly, his head crashing against the doors of the bus as he landed in a heap on the steps. Pulling the doors open I stamped hard firstly into his scarred face and again onto his arm feeling it break under my booted foot. Feeling satisfied that he wouldn't be attempting to kill me again that day; I kicked him out of the bus on to the side of the road. As the fanatic landed on the road, the driver put the bus into gear and we pulled away. I picked up the big blade that had fallen at the front of the bus and (noticing it had a trickle of my blood on it) threw it out of the vehicle.

For the rest of the trip, my fellow passengers remained inert as I sat applying pressure to the wound on my neck and wishing that I had a mirror so that I could see just how bad it was (or hopefully that it was indeed just a small slice and nothing to worry about!)

Arriving back at the camp in Moyana late afternoon (after begging a lift back from a contact in Nabwana), I walked in to the training hall.

I had left my room key in my desk before setting off on the "training activity" and I needed to get cleaned up.

Nobody was about in the hall so I grabbed my keys and walked across the gym to go back to my room. As I did so I had to pass a large mirror and decided to check the neck wound - it looked deeper than I'd hoped it was. Even though I had stemmed the bleeding, I headed straight for the medical centre instead.

Five incredibly neat stitches and an awkward shower later (trying to keep my neck dry), I was sat telling the tale of my adventure to Will Boato and Johan in the dining hall over a large bowl of rice, vegetables and goat meat. Will explained that the scar faced man would probably have been a member of one of several militant guerrilla organisations from around Samawi and that he would have targeted me, not because I was white and looked so out of place, but because I was wearing an army issue uniform and therefore representing the government!

It didn't make me feel any better, but at least I understood that it wasn't anything personal.

Three days later Marc and Suzi arrived at the camp on their bike laden down with more saddle bags, tank bags and back packs than looked safe or comfortable. By chance, it happened that when they arrived at the gates, Joe and Billy were there to meet them. The big Swede recognised them immediately from my description of the pair in my reports of my trip. Joe knew that I'd arranged things with Will Boato for the visa that the Dutch couple were so anxious for and, on sending Billy to fetch me from the training hall, immediately took advantage of the situation.

In the time it took me to get to the dining hall where I'd been told to meet them, Marc and Suzi had been made to feel so indebted that they had been relieved of a half bottle of Glenfiddich, a packet of Belgian chocolates, a pair of long fat Cuban cigars and a very battered acoustic guitar to demonstrate their gratitude. No matter how much I insisted that it really wasn't necessary they were adamant that they wanted me to accept the gifts. It really was quite a ransacking, even for a Viking! But, the Dutch bikers went on their way complete with Visa and big smiles, so everybody was happy in the end.

That night on the beach I sat sharing the chocolates, cigars and excellent single malt with Johan; we'd learnt that we could manage about six and a half songs between us on the guitar (allowing for plenty of bum notes and mis-played chords). I got by with butchered versions of Dylan's "Blowing in the Wind", Free's "Alright Now", Lennon & McCartney's "Norwegian Wood" and the first bit of Led Zeppelin's "Stairway to Heaven" and Joe could play (using the term loosely) The Animals' "House of the Rising Sun", Pink Floyd's "Wish you were Here" and what came to be known as the 'Swedish Acoustic' version of Thin Lizzy's "Whisky in the Jar". Over the coming years we never really became better players, but the battered old guitar spent many a happy drunken night around beach fires with assorted people strumming away with varying degrees of talent.

CHAPTER FIVE

(November 1983)

I was literally shaken awake – the whole building had shuddered. I could hear gunfire! I threw some clothes and my boots on as quickly as I could and ran out of my room at exactly the same time as Johan came out of his door.

"What the fark is happening?" he asked still looking half asleep, "are we under farken attack?"

"It would appear so Joe my man," I replied with only a hint of sarcasm, "that's one of the things I like about you – always quick on the uptake!"

"Go fark yourself you English rose!" came his eloquent response.

We had spent the whole of August and September a couple of months earlier with the elite of Samawi's armed forces training in the use of firearms. I had at first not been particularly keen on this but had decided, after hearing tales of more frequent rebel attacks on our guys, that it might actually be useful to have something to settle an argument with if I couldn't convince my opponent with my fists and feet. Now I carried a Kalashnikov slung over my shoulder every time I left the base. The training had surprised me, it had been a lot more about being able to think correctly in pressure situations than the non stop target practice and 'care of your weapon' stuff that I had expected. Although there had been a great deal of the typical Hollywood image of physical conditioning and mental torment and the obligatory runs with heavy packs up and down sand dunes, the big Swede and I had relished these challenges and had entered into the exercises with almost fanatical enthusiasm. This had led to much annoyance from the regular troops that were taking part, which in turn had led to the two of us working even harder.

As I stood there looking at my Swedish friend (both of us brandishing the Russian weapons) the gunfire began again from the direction of the base's main gates. We stealthily made our way towards that area. Noticing that half of the office block attached to our dormitory wing had been turned to rubble by mortar fire; I picked up the pace and simultaneously raised my alertness level.

We reached the main courtyard to find a battle scene; some of our lads were holed up in the offices in the reception area, another group of six or seven were behind a couple of trucks half way across the yard between the buildings and the gates. More soldiers were streaming into the area from varying angles from the dormitory wings and officers' digs.

Billy Whizz and Michael (who was at the time in temporary command as Will Boato was on leave) reached us at a time when my mouth must still have been open with the shock and realization of the seriousness of the situation. "Are you two OK?" Michael asked, I wasn't sure whether he was deliberately not singling me out, or if the Swede looked as shocked as I did. "Err…yeah!" we answered in unison. "Good! Go with Billy." he ordered.

Billy led us and twelve others back around the other side of the main building where he stopped to explain that a unit of rebel guerrillas (he estimated about fifty militia men) were attacking from outside the gates and along the walls spread over about four to six hundred metres along the perimeter. Michael was going to organise an increase in firepower from the courtyard. Our group were going over the wall and circling around to the rear of the guerrilla unit 'taking out' any rebels that we happened to bump into along the way. It didn't cross my mind for a minute that this was not my fight, or even that I had come out here to be a better martial artist not to take part in gun battles. I didn't have the ability to think anything other than directing all my focus and concentration on the task in hand. After all, this was my home now and these were my friends, we were under attack and I actually wanted to deal with the situation. Yes, I was scared – absolutely fucking terrified. Fear was racing through every vein and nerve ending in my body – but along with the fear was an excitement. This was another test of my skill in combat and hadn't I always wanted to be the best that I could possibly be. Hadn't I always said that everybody should live for the moment? As my thought process worked through the confused, terrified and exhilarated mass of mental standpoints, our group started to move away. Billy leading us into battle, we were split into three groups of five, one leading, one shadowing at a short distance and the other group tailing. Johan and I were in the lead group with Billy and two other guys we knew from training them in unarmed combat (I remembered their names as they would have been bullied terribly at any English school in the 1970's. Samawians did have a tendency to use very old-fashioned British names for their male offspring), Herbert and Cedric!

We had managed to make about twenty metres from the outside of the wall with gunfire raging from the direction of the main gates when a group of seven rebels came running over the brow of a small hill straight towards us. They were more surprised to see us than we were to see them, so we reacted first – they didn't stand a chance. All five of us had fired at the seven men so I couldn't be absolutely certain that I had actually killed any of them, but my heart knew. It was like no other emotion that I had ever experienced before. I wasn't stupid enough to think that if it had been the other way around that the man who could have killed me would have given my corpse a second thought – but it was still bizarre, and incredibly I knew that I would probably have to repeat the experience a few more times before I could get back to more 'normal' times!

We moved on. The realisation dawned on me that more rebels could possibly have heard our shots. But the noise from the base's courtyard had not lessened at all so maybe we were in luck. We approached the top of the hill that the rebels had run over a few minutes before and Billy and Cedric crawled up to see what awaited us on the other side. Herbert, Johan and I all held back a few metres. I took a second or two to glance at my Viking friend and knew immediately that he was having just as hard a time of things as I was, probably the exact same thoughts and inner battles. Herbert on the other hand appeared calm and composed;

this was by no means his first experience of such bloodshed. Billy signalled for us to join them at the hilltop, from where we could see the gates and into the courtyard. A few bodies lay either side of the gates, death on both sides. A fleeting thought passed through my troubled mind, wondering if any of my friends were amongst the dead.

Billy pointed out three separate groups of rebels. A group of six to our right had set themselves along the top of a building overlooking the courtyard and appeared to be doing not much else other than firing sporadically to add to the confusion amongst our guys down there. A second rebel group of what only looked like three or four were in a small copse about a hundred metres further to our right. A lorry was parked up close by so we had to suspect there could be a few more men in the vehicle. The remainder of the guerrilla unit was spread around the gates of the base; we estimated that there were about twenty still active in that group.

Billy looked pensive for only a short space of time before ordering Herbert and Cedric to join the other two groups together and attack the rebel units at the base's gates from the rear as planned, but, to wait for fifteen minutes before doing so. Then, gesturing for Johan and I to follow him, he moved away back down the hill stopping at the bottom to fill us in on his plan. We were to 'take out' the rebels in the trees and then get to the six men on the roof before Herbert and Cedric et al began their attack. Another fleeting thought passed through my troubled mind: "all of a sudden Andy Hopwood is James fucking Bond!"

And then we were off, moving through the dawning morning as swiftly yet silently as we could. We stopped at a hillock some thirty metres from the copse, we'd circled around from our position on the hill top in order to approach unnoticed. Billy had a last look at the men in the copse before telling us his plan. I was to circle around to the other side of the trees and wait for his signal before moving in. Joe and Billy were going in to check for any additional men in the truck before hitting the rebels in the trees. So his signal was to be a gunshot. It didn't sound like much of a plan to me, but not having any better ideas myself, I went along with it. Billy and the Viking went one way and I went the other – after a few strides fear rose up in my throat like bile.

"Fuck!" I thought, "Now I'm on my own."

I had no choice but to go with the plan, but was already regretting not coming up with a better one.

I reached the other side of the trees and lay down cradling the Kalashnikov and desperately trying to find religion while watching the men in the copse. I reminded myself the message that had been repeated over and over in our firearms training: "guerrilla units don't take prisoners – it's always kill or be killed!"

From my position I could see exactly what they were doing, on the ground lay the missile launcher that had obviously done the damage to the base's office block; the three guys seemed to be trying to repair it.

I could just about make out the truck on the other side of the trees and hoped that Billy and Joe would get there undetected. I didn't have to wait very long to find out. Four men jumped from the back of the vehicle, two of them were dead before they hit the ground, the shots from my friend's guns jolting me into action. Before I could think "Shit, this wasn't the way it was meant to happen!" I was up and running in to the trees firing at the guys who were reaching for their own weapons – they didn't get to them.

Nothing was said between the three of us as we moved from the trees in to the truck (the keys had been in the ignition) and started to drive back towards the base for part two of Billy's plan. We all knew that the rebels had been killed because it was them or us. But, that really didn't make me feel any better. The worst part was there was more to come.

We parked at the front of the building, on the roof of which were the six gunmen. Billy looked at his watch and whispered that we had five minutes before Herbert and Co. were going to attack the rear of the guerrilla unit at the gates. I couldn't believe that it had only been ten minutes since we left the hilltop. Fear is an amazing emotion; it really fucks with your mind!

We began to climb on to the top of the truck for our roof top rendezvous.

Most of the men on the roof were totally focused on the action in the courtyard. We opened fire as soon as they came into sight but one of them had heard us and managed to turn his rifle to get a shot off. Billy flew spinning from the roof top as he was hit; the man paid for his awareness and fast reflexes by dying in a writhing, twitching, bloody mess as Joe held his finger on the trigger aiming the Kalashnikov at the rebel's chest.

After an extremely short period of time there was nobody else left alive on the rooftop apart from two confused Europeans. We were both in shock; neither of us expected the carnage that had happened that morning. As we stared at each other the gunfire erupted again at the gates; Billy's plan was working!

"Billy!" I shouted realising that we hadn't checked if our friend was actually dead or alive. As we looked over the edge of the roof where he'd fallen, I was both amazed and relieved to see him lying smack bang in the centre of the truck's roof. He was moving, as I reached his side I could see that the rebel's shot had hit him in the shoulder, his collar bone smashed by the bullet, was visible through his blood soaked shirt and he was still bleeding profusely. I stemmed the blood flow with my T-shirt and cursed at the fact that we had gone in to this situation without field dressings or any other supplies. With a great deal of aggravation, difficulty and pain for Billy, we managed to get him off the roof and into the back of the truck. By the time we'd achieved this, the battle was over.

Forty-six guerrillas and twelve Samawi soldiers lost their lives in that morning of chaos, all of them with families and loved ones.

I went home on leave a few weeks later, still battling to cope with my newfound ability to kill. Nothing had been reported on the UK news; nobody at home knew anything about the events of that morning. Was it that insignificant and inconsequential?

CHAPTER SIX

(January 1984)

I was stood in an office overlooking the courtyard and main gates; the bullet holes and damage from that terrible morning still in evidence in many places. The building work to rebuild the main office block further into the base appeared to be progressing nicely. I was talking to Billy who, although very limited with his movement (to say the least) was back working in an administration job until he was back to full fitness. He was in exceptionally good humour for a man that had recently been shot. I'd been telling him about my trip back to England over Christmas. It had been nice to get away for a while (apart from the loving reception from my Grandparents, I had felt "in the way" as far as the rest of my family had been concerned). I'd always been a bit of a 'black sheep' but this had felt like I'd developed a bad case of the plague!

I'd managed to have a few nights out with some of my old friends and had temporarily rekindled a relationship with a former girlfriend (very temporarily). It had lasted for at least three hours (and several free drinks for her in a night club) until as we were leaving she told me, "thanks for the drinks sucker, but there's no way that I'll ever forgive you for deserting me to go to Africa and I will pissing well hate you until the day that you die." She was a nice girl!

So after spending a full day lazing around on my Grandparent's sofa, "chewing the fat" with my Grandad and being served endless cups of tea, sandwiches, cakes and other goodies by my Nan, I visited Griff. We both got incredibly drunk to celebrate the birth a few months earlier of his daughter Rebecca.

The following morning, suffering with a bastard of a hangover, I said my goodbyes to my parents and flew out of the cold British Winter (which I had begun to hate with a passion) back to the sizzling heat of Africa. I spent the flight wondering about my Mum and Dad. I knew they loved me in their own way and that I had never been the easiest kid to handle, but why couldn't they just be a little more demonstrative. I knew that they hated me being in Africa, but why not at least talk about it? Every time that I'd tried to raise the topic they would always change the subject or make their excuses to leave the room – complete denial!

As Billy and I were talking, a flashy red sports car raced in through the gates and skidded to a stop on the far side of the courtyard. The unmistakable figure of Joe unfurled himself as he climbed out. I went across the yard to greet him and find out where he'd acquired the wheels. He explained that his parents had been very generous with his Christmas money that year and putting that together with his savings he'd managed to find an exclusive garage in Nabwana where he'd bought the car. He'd spent all of that morning acquiring all of the requisite documents to allow him to drive legally in Samawi, and had just enjoyed the open (if uncared for) roads for the fifty miles back to our base in Moyana. It was indeed a beautiful machine, but I couldn't help but wonder what the hell use it would be to him in this country. It did not matter, he was happy.

For the next few days we settled back in to the routine of running the unarmed combat training in the main training hall. We heard regular reports of battles in varying areas as the guerrilla militia increased their efforts. There was a definite increase in activity around the base too. The large car park at the rear of our training hall had been transformed into an extension of the military driving school and instead of jeeps and Land Rovers there were scores of tanks and armoured cars either parked up or moving back and forth from the surrounding grounds of the base.

Where as before the base would sometimes be quiet, now there was always the buzz of activity and the drone of vehicles moving.

After a few more days (all of which with Joe disappearing at every opportunity to drive his new toy) I finished my usual run down to the beach, trained on my own, and ran back towards the training hall to shower and begin the days instructing. As I turned the corner to the hall's entrance I noticed that the big roller shutter door was open (this was a rare occurrence –it had happened only once before since I'd been there and that was for a delivery of some new equipment). I walked in to find the big Swede vacuuming the inside of his car which was parked at the end of the gym on the polished sprung floor – a step too far I decided.

"Joe, my man – you can't fucking park that there mate!"
I shouted at him over the din of the vacuum.

"I'm just about finished." he laughed slapping me on the
shoulder "I thought that I'd get it done before you got here."
he said as though that would be okay.

"Even so, you're taking the piss – get it moved before Will
Boato turns up and kicks you and the car back to Scandinavia
– you can't fuckin' park it there mate!" I reiterated.

"I know – you've already farken said that." he laughed
and slapped me again, then he turned the vacuum off and
jumped into his pride and joy and drove out of the hall.

I showered, calmed down and began to sort through the
day's itinerary. The big Swede came back in to the hall, "hey
man I'm sorry," he said "I shouldn't have driven the car in
here – if anyone else was to do that I would go farken mad,
it won't happen again eh."

We left it at that and got on with the day's training.
It was a pretty uneventful morning with a group of new
recruits apart from one incident when we were teaching
a break-away move and a member of the group decided to
question the effectiveness of the technique. This was usually
something that we encouraged; any debate on such matters
was normally seen as healthy. The new recruit in this case
however, had been demonstrating an incredibly bad attitude
from the moment he walked in; he was arrogant, mouthy
and obnoxious. The other lads in the group had shown that
they were fed up with his antics, but nobody had said too
much and he had carried on regardless (possibly because he
was a relatively huge guy). He was about six feet tall and
I guessed about eighteen stone, which made him just a bit

bigger than Joe and a great deal bigger than me and most of the group of recruits.

The technique was a simple one – a quick but effective escape from a choke hold which requires no size or strength if performed correctly – and the big recruit watched me demonstrate the method and talk through the finer points. He then proceeded to walk towards me with a mocking smile. "Little man," he scoffed, "do you think that a small thing like you could get away from Manno the muscle man?" he laughed and kissed his over developed bicep.

I looked at Joe; he smiled and gave me the slightest of nods to my questioning raised eyebrow.

I turned back to the huge recruit, "Manno, is that your name?' I asked

"Manno the muscle man!" he corrected me, again kissing his bicep.

"Well Manno, congratulations on your wonderful physique – you have obviously spent a lot of time throwing weights around. But, to answer your question, yes I could escape and all that wonderful muscle won't count for shit if you've got no idea whatsoever how to use it to good effect!" I had his full attention now, "put the choke hold on," I told him – he did, and he was just as strong as he looked he lifted me off the floor by the neck – I smiled, and a question flickered across his eyes. In the next couple of seconds I had escaped from his grasp and put him on the floor at my feet. "Size can be an advantage Manno my friend." I told him, "But knowledge, experience and technique are the most essential elements in a fighter's arsenal!"

By lunchtime we had forgotten all about the car incident and went off to the dining hall. After a hefty helping of a strange looking and weirdly textured stew type meal served with a grunt by the usual suspects of the kitchen staff, Joe and I returned to the training hall to prepare for the afternoon sessions. After a quick look at the diary and student files in the office we went back into the gym area to meet the "victims" for the afternoon. Joe began his introduction speech to let those in attendance know what they had let themselves in for, when suddenly there was a massive noise and the whole of the side of the training hall came crashing inwards! The group of soldiers moved as one away from the incoming wall and managed to avoid being crushed by the falling brickwork (one or two suffered cuts and bruises, but nothing major). My first thoughts were of a guerrilla mortar attack and I moved swiftly in the direction of the stash of firearms locked at the far end of the hall, signalling for others in the group to follow me. As I glanced back towards the wall that was still falling, I could not believe what I was seeing: the brickwork fell away to reveal one of our own Samawian tanks that had apparently lost control and crashed into (and straight through) the wall! Joe was moving like a possessed man in that direction. The bricks were now only falling in ones and twos as the tank had come to a halt. The big Viking sprang on to the top of the tank and as he did so, the driver, looking confused, bewildered and bloodied popped his head up like a rabbit with meximatosis. Joe grabbed the unfortunate guy by the scruff of his neck and, with a massive grin on his face, started shouting, "you can't farken park that there mate!" slapping him around the head to punctuate every syllable.

The whole situation was incredibly comical and I had to laugh. The group of students were still cheering and ridiculing the dazed driver when his superior officer clambered over the rubble to bring even more pain and misery into his life.

The builders who were already working at the base had suddenly become busier and the driver who had been a new recruit to the tank regiment found himself in the military prison for his use of 'banned substances' whilst on duty. Joe and I found ourselves instructing most of our training sessions in the open air of the base's football pitch beyond the assault course.

A few weeks later, on a long weekend off, I went with Joe, Michael and Joseph for two days of climbing on the slopes of Mount Nabinda followed by a day sky diving over the Great Nomali River. Michael had managed to blag permission to use a chopper from Will Boato and so we flew down country for the climbing which introduced me to some of the most fabulous scenery that I'd ever had the privilege to see: a spectacular mountain overlooking vast plains of lush green landscapes and some seriously challenging routes to climb too.

We then flew across country for the skydiving day. Joe had missed out on the last sky diving trip to the Nomali region – you'll recall that he'd opted to try a different kind of 'jump' with the lovely Georgia much to the annoyance of her father and family – but the spectacular scenery and the buzz of free-falling over the massive river was as mind-blowing for me second time around as it was for him on his first trip.

This was to become a regular routine for the four of us on our long weekend breaks.

On our return to the base in the early hours of Monday morning (we weren't due to start work again until Tuesday), noting that the builders were making good progress, the office block was nearing completion and the training hall looked like it could stand up on it's own again too! I told Joe that I was driving in to Nabwana later to visit the market. "I will drive you Andy – show you how a real farken car moves eh!" he told me. I let the comment about the car pass as I would be glad for the company.

After grabbing a few hours sleep, I was woken by the sound of the big Swede banging on my door shouting, "farken wake up Andy, come and see what the farken hell those farkers have done to my farken car!"

I shouted at him to shut up for a minute and let him in; I threw some clothes and boots on while listening to him rant on incoherently. As soon as I was ready he led the way to his car. I couldn't help myself, I literally fell over laughing. This made him even more incensed and he booted me in the back. I didn't blame him, I'm sure I would have done the same had it been the other way around, so I stood up, and trying to keep my face straight listened to him seethe and swear about the state of his new car.

He had parked it for the weekend on the main courtyard. What he hadn't realised was that a family of black vultures had taken up residence in the tree under which he had parked the shiny red vehicle; it was now totally covered in approximately three millimetres thick of vulture droppings, it did not look good. I left him to sulk and endeavour to clean the shit off the car, while I took an army jeep into Nabwana.

When I got back that evening, Joe was still seriously pissed off. The paint work was mostly fucked; two of the vultures had been shot, three others had flown off never to be seen again!

I cheered him up a little by showing him a bottle of Single Malt whisky that I'd bought on my trip and we wandered down to the beach to mull over the weekend's events while sipping at the smoky amber liquid.

CHAPTER SEVEN

The most stupendous hangover in the history of the world had decided to take up residence just behind my eyes! It was now the first week of February, and the night before had seen a small-scale gathering of friends celebrate my nineteenth birthday with some large-scale alcohol abuse! Will Boato had arranged for a party to be held in his quarters, which was a relatively large apartment next to the main office buildings in the base. Michael and Joseph had supplied far too much of the evil local liquor and there had also been copious amounts of wine, beer and whisky that Joe and Billy's wife Paula had bought from a family friend in Nabwana – Paula had also made a huge pan of a spicy stew that was simmering over a fire in Will's yard; it was delicious.

But now, the morning after the night before I was suffering from the resulting dehydration with a bastard of a headache and the ability to shit through the eye of a needle. All that was tied in with the knowledge that Will Boato had something not particularly pleasant in store for me; he'd mentioned at the party that he wanted a meeting with Joe and I, along with Billy and a few other guys at noon that day in his office. He had told me that he had a "proposal" for us. This (I'd begun to learn) usually meant that it would be painful, would put my life in danger or, more often than not, both.

I recoiled as the door to my room was nearly knocked off its hinges and a large Swede shouted "Wakey-Wakey Andy my man – time to get up!" I opened the door as quickly as I could. "Shut the fuck up!" I told him.

We went for a run along the beach to try and get the blood moving enough to shift the excess alcohol – it helped a little; so we ate some fresh fruit from the trees by the pond and some warm bread from the kitchens before showering and, feeling a bit more human, went along to discover what Mr. Boato was going to rope us into!

Two hours later; twelve of us were sat around a table in the dining hall eating a dour-looking but tasty mixed bean salad, and talking through the likely consequences of the fact that we had all just agreed to take part in Will Boato's latest plan in his war against the rebel militia. I looked at the people around that table, I knew all of them – Louis, Jonathan, Freddie and Juan were all from the Paratroop regiment and had been with us on a few of our long-weekend escapades to jump over the Great Nomali River. Benni, Paul, and Henry had all been members of the same unit as my old adversary Isaac (who was now incarcerated) but they had all proven to have a much better attitude than that bastard. They had often attended unarmed combat training sessions that I had been leading and had proven to be both respectful and sociable. They had also been part of the instruction team that had trained Joe and I in our weapons training. They had proven then to be very knowledgeable and supportive. There was also Michael, Joseph and Billy who I now considered to be close friends. Finally there was Johan and me. Will Boato had just informed us that we were the twelve members of Samawi's brand new 'Special Task Force!'

The twelve of us had been chosen for our various specialist skills and abilities, as well as our overall capabilities in a pressure situation, and also our aptitude to be able to work as part of a team when necessary. We were to continue with our usual 'day jobs' but Will had told us that he would expect us to carry out dedicated assignments as required based on 'intelligence' that he received concerning the guerrilla forces.

My thoughts and emotions were all over the place: fear (this was no doubt going to lead to more danger than I'd ever known before), excitement (I was still young and foolish enough to get excited about danger), anger (at myself for agreeing to be a part of it at all), pride (that I had been chosen ahead of many more experienced men) and there was also another feeling – a sense of belonging. Somehow it seemed that this was where I was meant to be, this didn't happen to me in England, at the place that I had previously called 'home'. Looking at the faces around that table, and pondering over my emotions, I realised what I had found, a place where I actually fitted in.

It was another two weeks before Samawi's Special Task Force had it's first call in to action. We had sat through a myriad of meetings and had spent every spare moment in each other's company, either training at one skill or another, or just socially. This had proven very useful in getting to know each other's quirks, faults and foibles. There was a definite underlying feeling that we all wanted something to happen – we actually wanted that call to arms!

A detachment of Guerrillas were known to be operating from the town of Cabilo, one hundred and seventy five miles west of our base. Our information was that they had an arms stash at a furniture factory (which apparently was managed by the father of one of the rebel leaders) and the building was also known to be utilized as the HQ of the rebel force in that region. Our mission was to enter the factory at night, find and retrieve whatever information and evidence possible and then destroy the weapons, ammunition and the factory. The government would then have the factory rebuilt under supervision using the insurance money, happy in the knowledge that they had made a big hole in that section of the rebel army.

So at dusk, with a head full of orders and information, I found myself outside the window of what appeared to be a large carpentry shop in Cabilo. The familiar smell of timber fleetingly reminded me of my cabinet-making Father's workshop at home before I snapped my focus back to the matters in hand. Billy, Joe, Michael and I had made the initial 'reccy' at the rear of the building and were looking for the quietest place to gain entry now that we were as sure as we could be that we were only going to meet with "limited resistance." Louis, Jonathan, Freddie and Juan were undertaking the same task at the front of the factory and the other four members of the team were to "keep an eye on matters" from surrounding advantage points. This basically meant eradicating anybody who wasn't on our side, and to move swiftly ("run like fuck") to help us out if the shit hit the fan!

The door was open, a light shone out onto the step from inside, Billy and Michael were either side of the doorway. The voices of at least three men could be heard from my position next to Joe on the fire escape stairway. I tentatively tried the fire door, it moved just a fraction of a centimetre – it was unlocked! I nodded to Joe, who in turn signalled to Billy and Michael that we were ready to go – the signals were then relayed by Benni and Joseph to the guys at the front of the building and I hoped like hell that they were ready. I wanted this anxiety phase over – I was definitely an action or inaction kind of guy. I never like the anticipation of an event – I wanted to either get on with it or go the fuck home!

"OK – Let's farken do it!" Joe whispered to me as he received the signal to move in. I pulled the door open slowly and carefully, the last thing we needed was rebels inside reaching for their weapons because they'd heard us coming in. I led the way along what I thought appeared to be an indoor balcony type walkway that led to an office suspended on steel girders at one end (door open and no light on) and a stairway leading down to the main carpentry workshop below. As Joe and I edged slowly along the walkway, I could see two shadows move in through the doorway at the rear of the shop floor. Looking towards the front end, I could also make out two more figures moving out of the light into cover of darkness. I was confident that there were also another two, I wasn't too concerned that I couldn't see them – that was meant to be the idea after all. Six men stood around a large workbench away to my left, there appeared to be several sheets of paper and two rifles on the bench. None of the men were obviously armed otherwise, but we had to believe they all had concealed weapons. This was no time for complacency. Joe had moved in front of me and was at the office door looking in – he shook his head – it was empty.

We made our way back along the walkway and, leaving the big Swede at the top I started to move down the stairs one at a time. Joe would watch the ground level and follow me once I was down safely. I focused on moving quietly and unseen. Suddenly there was a loud crashing noise; I froze. Two more men appeared from out of what could only be described as a trap door which had been thrown open, then another two men; they were swiftly followed by yet another two. Still without moving, I waited to see what would happen – the six newcomers all moved quickly towards there colleagues at the workbench. There was a great deal of hurried, excitable and mumbled conversation amongst the twelve men. I started to fear the worst, had someone been spotted outside? Had they had a warning about our raid? Then, a burst of laughter broke the air and the group of twelve moved in to a closer huddle around the papers and map to continue their discussion. I finished my descent of the stairs and was soon joined by Joe. We quickly found cover. As we did so, four of the rebels moved away and back towards the trap door, two others were heading straight towards the stairway that we'd just moved away from. This left six still at the bench. The four men descended through the trap door pulling it closed behind them with the same loud crash. As the sound echoed around the factory the two men who had made it as far as the bottom of the stairway were stopped in their tracks by a big Viking and a scrawny long-haired Englishman hanging off their necks and sending them to sleep by cutting off the blood supply to their brains. Dropping them into the darkness of the shadows (in more ways than one), we turned to see six figures at the edge of the light where there were still six rebels at the work bench. As Joe and I moved to join them, the two rifles were confiscated by the diminutive figure of Billy who suddenly appeared. Just as swiftly, five more of our team appeared to present five of the shocked rebels with their fate. That however still left one man standing and even though I was moving with speed to back my friends up (with a Viking at my heels) the last standing rebel had begun a warning shout and had turned before I could reach him. His shout was cut off almost as soon as it started by my fist being smashed into his throat and crushing his voice box along with his windpipe – the rasping sound as he fell was soon drowned out by the crashing sound of the trap door once again being thrown open and the four rebels appeared with rifles. This I noticed through the agony that had overwhelmed me as the falling man with the crushed throat delivered his final "fuck you" by ramming a steel spike into my left leg, just above the knee. I tried to stay upright but the pain was too immense and I fell to the ground, finding myself staring into the vacant unseeing eyes of the man who'd stuck me with what I later discovered to be a carpenter's braddle. I shouted, "fuck you too!" but my voice was drowned out by the gun battle that was being waged on the other side of the factory floor. I rolled away to my left and managed to position myself under the workbench that had featured so heavily in the night's events. I could see that there was activity outside the doors of the factory and I hoped that Joseph and the guys outside were okay. Trying to stem the flow of tears that the pain shooting from my leg to every sinew of my body was creating, I found a piece of wood large enough to enable me to keep myself upright. I had just managed to get to my feet when the gun fire stopped. I looked across to see Joe, Billy and Jonathan. The rear doors flew open and five more rebels stormed through. I spotted the glint of steel as they made it into the lighted area, two of them didn't make it any further as bullets met their charge; two more were met by Joe and Jonathan and didn't get any further. The remaining man did get as far as where I stood, but was met with my newly found piece of wood.

The following day, back at base, the Samawian Special Task Force was counting the costs of its first successful mission.

Henry and Freddie had been killed. Freddie had run towards the trap door as the rebels had opened fire; Henry had been killed by a knife man outside the doors as he and the rest of the guys from outside were coming to help us towards the end of the battle inside.

Billy, having only just recovered from the bullet hole in his shoulder had taken another bullet in the side of his waist. This time it had only skimmed the surface but it still left a nasty wound (it became a bit of a standing joke how he could be so small and yet such an easy target!)

Jonathan had an evil looking knife wound across his bicep from meeting the charging man head on.

Joe had two cracked ribs from diving in to a woodpile when the gunfire started ("better than being farken shot eh?" he had said afterwards).

And it would be a few weeks before I would walk without a limp too.

But the rebels stash – which was a real stockpile of ammunition, rifles, fuel, missile launchers and grenades - had been destroyed quite spectacularly in what was quite a lightshow as we drove away. We had also discovered some interesting information on the guerrilla network.

Will Boato overall was happy, he commended us on being exceptionally brave men.

Freddie and Henry had known the risks, as had we all. The rest of us would mend (and probably do it all again soon). There is a very thin line between bravery and stupidity.

CHAPTER EIGHT

(May 1984)

Iron Maiden's 'Piece of Mind' album was blasting out of the stereo in Joe's car as we drove into Nabwana. The amazing vocal talent of Bruce Dickinson telling all, "if you're gonna die; die with your boots on!"

Four of us were on a night out – Joseph, Joe, Jonathan and I - were all going to visit some of the Capitol city's finest drinking establishments (none of which were exactly neat and tidy, let alone smart or stylish) but they were better than anything our base town of Moyana had to offer. Joseph had the keys to his brother's flat in the city centre, so we had somewhere to crash out later (his brother was out of the country on business and, like a fool, had entrusted Joseph with caring for the place in his absence.)

Jonathan had grown up in Nabwana and was keen to show off his two new European friends to all his old mates in town. The night began with us visiting several small bars. I had become used to the fact that most bars in Samawi actually seemed more like small cafes or even somebody's living room. The local fire water was beginning to have it's usual effect and the novelty of two white foreigners was starting to ware thin with Jonathan's pals (although for a while I had felt like an exhibit in a freak show with everybody wanting to meet and talk to "the two white soldiers").   So we decided to move on to a club that we had been to a few times before – a larger venue that actually had a dance floor. The club had a bit more of the type of atmosphere you might expect in a nightclub: drunken people flirting, cavorting, fighting and throwing up – we loved the place!

As soon as we walked in to 'The Equator Bar' Joe nudged me and pointed on to the dance floor saying, "that's farken Georgia – I'm going to say hello!" before I could ask if he had thought the matter through, considering the resulting beating and lucky escape that he'd endured on the last occasion they'd spent some time together, he was in the middle of the dance floor 'doing the Viking boogie' with Georgia and her friends. I left him to it and joined Joseph and Jonathan at the bar.

Several crappy dance tunes later a sweaty Swede, Georgia and three friends joined us at the bar, downed a long cold beer each and dragged the rest of us back on to the dance floor to "get down to Iko Iko!" (As the DJ suggested).

We endured the dreadful tune and I was relieved that I wasn't the worst dancer in our little group. Alcohol was having its evil effect and the DJ wasn't helping matters by playing "Satisfaction" by the Rolling Stones as the next tune. Georgia's friends seemed a little shocked by my Mick Jagger impersonation as I strutted around the floor clapping my hands and sticking my lips out while trying to sing the classic Stones track. Joe however thought it was hilarious, and soon, Joseph, Jonathan and the big Swede were following and copying me as the Jagger impression became more and more vigorous and outlandish. This lasted for just a couple of minutes before a group of local guys decided they didn't think much of our behaviour and charged towards us intent on doing us harm. The first attacker was closest to me; he had a beer bottle in his hand and seemed determined to smash it over my head. I had other ideas and, stepping out of his way, kicked his knee hard bending it in a direction it wasn't designed to go. The bottle missed and he didn't get up in a hurry. In my peripheral vision, I saw Joseph throw another man over a table as yet another moved in front of me waving a knife towards my face. As I moved back slightly I was grabbed from behind in a strangle hold by someone else. The knife man grabbed my shirt with his empty hand and moved the blade towards my left eye, his accomplice was screaming down my ear at him, "do it!"

I took the decision that I really didn't want him to 'do it' and stamping on the man behind's foot and sinking my teeth into his arm, I simultaneously shoved my fingers in to the knifeman's eyes with as much force as I could. This caused him to scream and reel backwards. I didn't stop moving as I escaped from the stranglehold and broke the offending arm before the knife man leapt forwards again – I was a little late with my block but managed to avoid the blade being sunk to the hilt anywhere life threatening – and I met his forward momentum with my own bodyweight behind my forearm which I slammed full force into his face. As he lurched backwards, the knife was dropped and kicking him hard to make sure he didn't get up again, I guessed that this was probably a good time to leave.

My three friends (who had been going through a similar experience) had just arrived at the same conclusion and we all made it to the door at about the same time.

After visiting the hospital to have the knife wound in my thumb, a knife wound in Joe's forearm and the damage caused by a bar stool to Joseph's head stitched, we went back to the flat to sober up before driving back to Moyana in the morning.

As we left the flat around ten o'clock, the mid-morning sun hurting my eyes, we were met with the sight of five men laying into Joe's car with steel bars and big sticks. They were really going to town on the windows, lights and bodywork, smashing it beyond all recognition. Joe was first to them screaming that he was going to "farken kill the farken bastards!" closely followed by the rest of us. They'd seen and heard us coming however, and they were now facing us with the intent of using the weapons on us. I saw Joe move inside the arc of the "big stick wielding" first attacker. As he took control of the man's arms, Joe brought his head smashing down onto the bridge of the man's nose. I didn't have chance to see any more because as that happened another guy with a steel bar ran to meet me swinging the weapon back above his head with the intent of cracking my skull in two. Out of pure instinct, I moved in towards him and blocking his weapon arm with my left hand (trying to ignore the excruciating pain in my thumb), slammed the forearm of my right arm into the man's groin. He let out an awful sound as I continued my forward momentum lifting his leg high off the ground and slamming him to the floor. His head hit the asphalt with a solid blow and blood instantly began to flow onto the road. I turned to see Jonathan and Joseph trying to prize a crazed Viking away from the man whose head he had in his grasp and whose face he was continually pounding against the dented and crumpled bonnet of his ruined car! He finally relented from the onslaught and the now subdued group of men helped each other away from their crazed conquerors.

The men had been the same members of Georgia's family that Joe had escaped from about twelve months earlier; she had told them that we were in town and I guess it wasn't too difficult for them to track us down after that. I suggested that Joe should probably avoid her in the future as I felt that her family were just a little over protective – and it seemed as though they held a grudge too!

For a while after that, the unarmed combat training sessions led by Joe and myself had an almost comical feel to them, as my left hand was not a lot of use because of my damaged thumb, and the Swede's right arm was very sore from the knife wound on his forearm. Between us we only had one good pair of arms!

Our conditioning training had to be changed somewhat to allow the wounds to heal, so we cut down on the actual physical contact side of things and concentrated more on the intricate details of our technical ability. We spent a lot of time on cardio vascular fitness and endurance training.

At one time during this healing process we were sat around a fire on the beach one evening, talking to Billy about how we'd adapted our daily routine. Joseph and Michael were there too as were Paula and her sister Lucia. Billy suggested that we should try adding long jump in to our program. We laughed at the suggestion thinking it was said in jest, but Billy was deadly serious and started marking out a strip in the wet sand for a 'run up' towards the softer dry sand. He then walked purposefully back to the far end of the 'runway' and sprinting like a man possessed, ran and leapt like a gazelle on acid. After travelling an amazing distance in the air and landing in the soft sand swiftly got to his feet and smiling shouted, "who can beat that then?"

After several attempts at getting even somewhere close to Billy's mark in the sand from his first amazing leap, none of us had come within two metres of it apart from Lucia who had beaten all of the other men. Billy was finding the whole spectacle hilarious, mocking and ridiculing our prowess at the athletics event. We were all laughing, but we were somewhat puzzled as to how the little man was such a skilled long jumper. While Joe was determinedly trying to launch himself to at least beat the distance set by Lucia, Paula pulled me away from the rest of the group and told me that both Billy and Lucia were Samawian long jump champions when they were at college – this was how Billy and Paula had met.

I allowed the competition to continue for a while longer until I managed to get Joe's attention, whispering to him. I informed him of Billy's collegiate achievement and told him what I proposed to do about it. We seized the pocket-sized long jumper and, informing Joseph and Michael of Billy's former accomplishment, we carried the struggling figure off the beach and up the path to the pond and fruit trees. Joe and Michael held him down and stripped him naked while Joseph and I ran to fetch the two other items required for Billy's punishment. We returned armed with a wooden pallet and a reel of duck tape and proceeded to fasten the star shaped naked Billy to the pallet. His wife and sister-in-law seemed to find the whole thing extremely bewildering. By the time Billy was floating, fixed to the pallet in the centre of the pond, there was quite a crowd amongst the fruit trees equally as puzzled and mystified as Lucia and Paula. The two sisters eventually waded in to rescue the exposed figure (but not before a large number of people had witnessed the poor guy in all his glory). Billy was suitably chastised for his ego trip! The fun didn't last for too long...

CHAPTER NINE

I was in the shower, cleaning up after my usual morning run and training session on the beach. My thumb had now fully healed and the members of the Special Task Force were all back to full fitness and training together again at every spare moment. We'd talked through the loss of Henry and Freddie as a group and individually and had come to terms with the emotions and consequences of that previous mission.

As I covered myself from top to toe in lather from the shampoo and soap, my eyes closed and my mind somewhere else, there was a massive explosion from very close by shaking me back in to the reality that had become my life and causing me to curse out loud. I rinsed myself off and towelled the wettest bits of my body as quickly as I could manage, got boots, shorts and vest on and ran out of my room in to the chaos that the blast had caused. I met Joe in the corridor – the look that we exchanged as we'd come out of our respective doors speaking volumes – and we ran in the direction of the main gates without saying a word. Moving as quickly as we could through the mass of panicking soldiers and civilians that populated the base at that time each morning, we were joined by Joseph and Michael.

We reached the courtyard at the main gates where everything was total pandemonium. There were bleeding and wounded people all over the place, some being cared for, some crying out for help, some obvious fatalities, other people were running in all directions. A smouldering burnt out shell of a car stood smoking close to the reception doors and the offices over looking the area had been hit with such a blast that the walls had several substantial cracks running from the ground upwards. There wasn't a single window left with glass in its frame. As the four of us sprinted across the courtyard, three army ambulances raced in with sirens blaring and tyres screaming as they screeched to a halt in front of the main entrance. Billy and Will Boato ran from the doors to meet us and explained that the rebel guerrillas had set a car bomb which had been designed to coincide with the time when the soldiers' shifts changed and the civilians that worked in the offices were arriving for the day. This was the time that the bomb would cause most casualties.

The ambulance crews that had arrived were obviously insufficient for the number of wounded people in the courtyard and there were certainly more in need of help inside the office block, so the four of us set about helping the medics and applying the relevant field dressings or first aid care to anybody that was in need of treatment. Billy and Will went about the business of turning the chaos of the morning into an organized state of emergency.

There were so many horrific injuries caused by the blast, over the course of the morning we treated all types of wounds, from soldiers with shards of glass imbedded in their bodies, people with breaks and dislocations from falling or being blasted off their feet to middle aged ladies with their arms literally missing, having been blown off in the explosion!

When the panic had diminished and some form of order had been restored we were told that twelve people had died (eight of them civilians) and a further thirty-one were injured (nineteen of them civilians).

A week later the Samawian Special Task Force was travelling by Land Rover to Nabwana. We were joined by a team of four explosives experts. Our assignment was to gain safe access for the four men to an address in the Capitol city which had been identified as a guerrilla storage house for the rebel militia's explosives. We knew that it would be heavily guarded and that there were a vast amount of "things that go boom" kept at the address.

We left the explosives guys at a hotel on the edge of town and spent the next two days and nights in shifts observing the 'Bomb House'. We had another unit of men ready on 'code red' waiting for us to call them if needed.

There hadn't been a great deal of activity at the house during the two days. It was just another 'edge of town' house in Nabwana with a back yard, a porch out back and a balcony above the porch. There were at least six men there on a permanent basis with four big German Shepherd dogs and not a lot else other than all that highly explosive material. The six men all carried side arms, two always had Kalashnikovs with them. We knew that we couldn't go in all guns blazing for fear of blowing everyone in Nabwana to kingdom come, so we had to do it the "softly, softly way".

The two rebels armed with the Kalashnikovs were sat smoking and chatting on the porch area outside the house. I guessed that they were used to the fact that nothing much happened at a storage house and were too relaxed about keeping watch. I never got chance to ask them as Joe and I had crept up behind them and broke their necks before either of them could engross us with their conversation. Benni, Joseph, Juan, Paul and Louis joined us, and we circled around to our prearranged positions: Benni with Joseph to go in the back; Juan, Paul and Louis to enter around the front of the house and Joe and I were going in on the first floor via the balcony. Billy, Michael and Jonathan were with the explosive experts holding back until we had 'made good' the entry.

I climbed up on one side of the balcony; Joe climbed the other and we landed softly as we noticed the door was open. We stood to one side; I took a stone from my pocket, dropped it on the floor and waited. The man appeared gun first – I took the gun, Joe took his life and we moved in to the house.

Joe went in first; I followed two steps behind. The rebel that was about to shoot the big Swede in the back should have waited for a split second longer. He obviously knew that there was someone coming in, but hadn't waited to see if there were more than one. With his gun raised and the Viking about to be shot, I didn't have any choice; I launched myself at the man and took him to the floor in a rugby tackle. The gun had fired and then he'd dropped it as I hit him. But all hell was now being let loose downstairs (in the ensuing moments as I battled with the rebel I could hear dogs barking and shots firing) my opponent lost his struggle for life and

I joined Joe on his way through the room towards the noise below. As we reached the landing, there was a door to our left; the stairs were in front of us to the right. The gunfire had stopped downstairs; thankfully nobody had set off any explosives. Joe glanced down the stairs and nodded back to me. "It's okay – Benni and Louis are coming now – there's a farken dead dog at the bottom of the stairs!" he whispered with a sick grin on his face.

I motioned towards the door and stood to one side as the Big Swede moved to the other. I turned the handle and pushed the door open. Joe turned with the intent of moving forwards in to the room but was met with a German Shepherd Dog growling with its muzzle no more than an inch from his groin. I checked the room for rebels; it was full of explosives but thankfully, no men. I started to smile – then shock took over – looking at the dog snarling at the Swede's balls. It had a harness which was loaded with what could only be explosives.

"Joe - don't fucking move! The fucking dog is packed like a bomb." I told him.

"Where do you think I'm gonna farken go?" he asked

I started to pull my gun, but as soon as my hand moved the dog leapt at me knocking me backwards and pinning me with its slavering jaw in my face.

I heard a shout from the stairs; "bomb guys coming in!" Paul's voice called.

The dog pulled its head back as if it was about to eat my fucking face so I decided to test a theory that I remembered hearing as a school child. Without any hesitation I grabbed the vicious mutt's front legs and pulled them apart as hard as I could, rolling from underneath it as I heard it screech in agony and slump forwards. As it lay there whining in pain Joe shot the poor creature through the head.

"I thought you were going to cuddle that thing all farken night!" he jibed

"Shut the fuck up!" I told him.

Billy and Michael, followed by the explosives guys, came up the stairs. Michael explained that there were three dead dogs and four dead rebels downstairs with just a small amount of bomb making equipment and several large cans of petrol. "Take a look in there," I said pointing into the room that the crazed and booby-trapped canine had come out of.

"Yeah, but it's probably not a good time to light a celebratory cigar eh!" Joe added with his usual grin.

"Shut the fuck up!" replied Billy.

One of the bomb experts made safe the harness on the dog. There was enough material in that house to make a hundred of the devices that had been used in the car bomb at the base. We knew that it would more than likely have been used at some stage too, there were reports every day of Army bases, police stations, even hospitals and bus stations being bombed by the rebel forces, killing the innocent and creating turmoil.

We called in the other army unit and transported all of the material away for safe disposal.

I lay in bed that night troubled by the events of the mission. The usual effects of having taken a life were there; the torment and anguish that tortured my mind after such actions were now, to me, an expected suffering. There were professional people at the base that I could talk to if I ever felt that these emotions were out of control. So far, I'd pretty much managed them on my own or, at least once a month,

Joe and I would have a 'talk things through' drinking session on the beach.

The thing that was really difficult for me to understand was how and why the dog had been used in such a fashion. The rebels had obviously used the animal as what they saw as a 'last line of defence,' if anybody had got as far as that room, then obviously all the other guards (including the other dogs that had not been rigged) would have already been taken out. But it just seemed such a barbaric act, using an animal in that way – "me, talking about barbaric acts, wasn't it me that killed two people and the poor bastard dog that I am so concerned about today!" I thought. This was swiftly followed by, "I need a fucking drink!"

I dressed in T-shirt and shorts and grabbing a bottle of Glenlivet that I'd been saving for such an occasion, left my room and wandered towards the cliff tops by the fruit trees. As I approached, I noticed the silhouettes of two familiar figures that had beaten me to the position. As I walked on towards them, two more figures came out of the darkness to my right. I smiled at the two walking to greet me – Joseph and Michael - armed with more bottles of the local liquor that we had affectionately named 'the Dragon's Breath'. We laughed and went to join Joe and Billy on the cliff side.

Having talked things through with our friends and drunk ourselves into an incredible stupor, things were a little easier to deal with; but we all knew that there would be a next time, and soon.

CHAPTER TEN

(September 1984)

I sat staring at the beguiling sight of the South Atlantic Ocean lapping the white sand on the beach at Calo. I had returned from England to Samawi a week early from my scheduled three week leave and decided to drive down the coast in my newly allocated personal 'open top' Land Rover. I wanted to see the sights that I'd heard were some of the most beautiful that the country had to offer. I had not been disappointed, the coastal scenery as I'd driven down to Calo had literally taking my breath away. I found it hard to comprehend that a country so picturesque and magnificent in its landscape could have so much violence and hatred raging within it.

In my aborted trip back to Birmingham, I had been happy to see my family at first and to know that they were all healthy and safe. My parents had greeted me with their usual awkwardness, behaving as though I'd just returned from an extended school trip or an 18 to 30 holiday and I'd picked up something nasty along the way. My grandparents had been the loving, welcoming people that I'd always known, even though they did both take me to one side individually when they thought that the other wasn't looking, and tell me that I should call or write more often as " your Nan misses you terribly!" or "your Gramps worries about you!"

I'd visited Griff and his new family and a few other old friends and spent a lot of time in music shops buying all the latest releases in the 'Heavy Metal' chart – tricky to find in Samawi.

After struggling to communicate with my parents for a week or so, I had taken my Mother and Nan out for the day (which was a way of trying to get my Mum to relax a little and not treat me like a stranger). My Dad was working during the day and was unable to come with us, so I'd asked my Nan to join us. She treated me in the same way that she had always done and I thought if Mum saw this, then she may realise that (underneath the suntan) I was still the same person that I'd always been!

Mum however, hardly said three sentences directly to me all day, unless I'd asked her a direct question. To round my day off, that evening my Father was treating us to a 'family meal out'. It was Mum, Dad, my two sisters and me and a full evening of backhanded jibes, tactless subject changes and sneering taunts. Of course it may have been my imagination, or it may have been my own fault. Either way, I said my goodbyes to them that night, explained as far as I could to my Grandparents the next day and booked an earlier flight, and left them all behind to sit looking at the spectacular scenery of Calo in order to try and understand what the fuck was going on with my life. It wasn't really helping, but I felt a little better after a few days camping amongst the fig trees overlooking the bay and decided to head back to base ready to start working again.

Setting off at sunrise, after one last prolonged look over the bay, I drove along, enjoying the open roads and the wild and natural backdrop to my return journey, the latest Iron Maiden release 'Powerslave' blasting out of the Land Rover's stereo. Suddenly I felt like I was free from the worries of my family in England. This was my life and I intended to live it to the full in any way that I fucking well chose to. "I am a free man!" I shouted at the African sky.

Sixty miles into the trip, the sky grew dark and my first experience of African rain was something to behold indeed. This was a part of the world where it hardly ever rained, but when it did, it really came down with a vengeance! I had missed other rainy seasons by choosing holidays to coincide with them but I had not been ready for this unexpected accompaniment to my journey. Within seconds I was soaked like a drowned rat; the foot wells of the Land Rover were turned into puddles and I could hardly see where I was going. Iron Maiden were belting out 'Rime of the Ancient Mariner' and I laughed out loud, "I know how he fucking felt!"

I drove back through the gates of the base, the warm rain still hammering down. I drove through the camp to get as close to my quarters as I could manage. I needed to be wrung out, my long hair was stuck to my head and back, my vest and shorts were stuck to my body. The Land Rover needed to be bailed out, but that would have to wait until the rain stopped. "Convertibles!" I smiled as I parked and walked towards my quarters.

As I opened the outside door to the corridor that led to my room, two men stood up from where they had been seated on the floor. I didn't recognise them, but one had a familiar look about him.

Dripping water all over the floor I looked at them both and asked,

"hi guys, I don't think you should be in here - are you lost or something?"

The two men exploded towards me, both pulling knives from their belts as they moved. I instinctively circled to the left to at least give me a chance of keeping one behind the other allowing me to deal with one at a time. The closest man's blade came towards my neck with a backhanded slashing motion. I moved in to block the attack and took control of the knife arm, keeping the man between his mate and me. I shouted at the second man, "stay back or I'll break his bastard arm!" He didn't stay back, so I made good my promise leaving the first man squirming on the floor. As the second man charged in with a downward stabbing motion, I managed to side step out of his way and hit him with a hooking kick between the shoulder blades to add to his forward momentum which took him through the flimsy glass of the window and out in to the pouring rain.

I turned my attention back to the first attacker who was now crying like a baby. "Would you like to tell me what that was about my friend?" I asked the man on the floor

"You can go and fuck yourself!" he told me impolitely.

I looked down at him shaking my head and placed my foot on his broken elbow which lay at an unsightly angle, "let me put it another way – what did you come here for?" I asked again. His screams were quite loud and had begun to attract quite a crowd, including Juan and Louis who had collected a very wet and bleeding second knifeman from outside.

"You destroyed my brother – I came to kill you!" He spat at my face, and as I dodged the phlegm, the family trait became apparent. "You are Isaac's brother." I said, "It seems that the intelligence level runs in the family."

"They're new recruits Joe," Louis informed me, "they came in two days ago."

"Third day – behind bars eh? That has to be some kind of record," laughed Juan grinning at me, "get yourself dry my friend, we'll take care of these two!"

"Thanks!" I smiled and went back to my room to shower and change.

The next morning, in the hot African sun that had returned after the torrential rain leaving the air smelling incredibly fresh, I had started to bail the water out of the foot wells of my Land Rover utilizing a small plastic bucket that I'd found in the storeroom of the training hall. The familiar sound of Swedish laughter came from the opposite side of the vehicle. I looked up to see Joe who had just returned from his leave with a mocking smile all over his face. "I've just seen Louis," he said, "he told me that you got a little wet, I've just spent three weeks in Sweden and I didn't see a single raindrop!" He was enjoying this, he had been allocated a Land Rover at the same time as I had, but he'd chosen a 'hard top' model – I had ridiculed him at the time.

"It's good to see you too!" I smiled, trying not to rise to the bait.

He watched me emptying the water for a minute or two longer before asking, "Can I get you a farken sponge?" As he started to laugh, a bucket full of the rain water hit him full in the face. Joe moved to retaliate for the soaking as

Billy appeared from around the corner at exactly the same moment. Billy told me that I was needed in Will Boato's office. As the big Swede moved towards me again I moved backwards and wagged my finger at him saying, "ah ah! Go and dry yourself off you big turnip – duty calls!" and with that I walked quickly to Will's office.

I knocked and walked in to see Will Boato looking a little troubled. He asked if I'd enjoyed my trip to Calo – he had grown up in that part of the country so he had been pleased that I had visited the area.

"The two young recruits that had the misfortune to encounter you last night, you know that one of them is Isaac's brother, the other his cousin I presume?" he began. I nodded – I somehow had thought that this was going to be about them.

"I do not believe that they are intrinsically bad people; a little misled, maybe foolish and certainly impetuous – but I don't think bad." he said looking at me waiting for my reaction. The fuckers had tried to kill me just a few hours ago and now I was being told they were just good kids making a mistake!

I smiled and shrugged saying, "okay, if I do buy that, what are you suggesting happens to them?"

"They won't be going anywhere for a little while Andy, they both need some recovery time in the hospital." he laughed quietly, "I don't think they realise how lucky they are that you didn't take their lives."

"They had our uniforms on." I said shrugging again. He smiled and continued, "I would like you to visit them and talk to them, see what kind of reaction you get. If they respond in a positive way, we'll let them continue with their basic training, if they break the rules again – I will hang their asses out to dry!"

I did as I'd been asked; I had roped Michael in to accompany me, visiting the two guys on a few occasions over the following week. They had looked horror stricken when I first walked in to the ward at the Military Hospital. At first the hatred was still there, but after bringing the conversation round to social and everyday matters and talking casually rather than officially, they lightened up and began to respond in a positive way, telling us of their ambitions to climb the ranks in the Army and make something of themselves.

On the third visit, as I walked in to the room the two guys were waiting for me, sat at a table in the centre of the ward. They had each written a letter of apology, asking for my forgiveness and condemning their behaviour. The letters explained that Isaac had goaded them into the attack when he heard that they were to be stationed at our base. They now realised that Isaac was the devil incarnate and that they now rued the error of their ways.

I reported back to Will Boato with the information and showed him the letters. I suggested that the two recruits should indeed be given a second chance. I did however; heavily recommend that they were given some form of special supervision. I do believe that some leopards have the ability to change their spots – I wasn't totally convinced however that they could achieve it with such speed!

CHAPTER ELEVEN

Nabwana airport was totally sealed off by the police and army personnel. In the Departures Lounge, guerrilla rebels held fourteen hostages and were demanding control of a plane and the release of six men who were members of their 'army' from a military prison just outside the conflict town of Cabilo. The six had been arrested two months previously at the same airport, when they were found to be in possession of guns, knives and other "un-tourist like" items when boarding two separate planes. Now a skilled negotiator was in contact with the leader of the group. Will Boato was with him in the Airport Manager's office. The rest of the Samawian Special Task Force and I were in positions around the perimeter of the building waiting for the order to move in. A team of police sharpshooters were also in position with what we were assured were clear views of the perpetrators.

I was positioned behind a large trailer which was full of luggage waiting to be taken to a plane due to depart. I had been there for twenty minutes – obviously it would be going nowhere for some time as the only people left anywhere within the airports perimeter fence were hostages, guerrillas, police or army personnel. I looked across to see Joe and Jonathan positioned alongside the double fire doors to my right; to my left were Paul and Benni positioned behind an airport fire truck. Billy, Michael, Joseph, Louis and Juan were all on the opposite side of the departures lounge in similar formation and positions. From where we were all situated we had a view of the proceedings that were happening inside. We estimated that there were only six rebels in that part of the building. The hostages were all being forced to sit against a wall on the East side of the floor area away to my left.

There was an awful lot of arm waving and aggressive gestures from the rebels inside. They were relentlessly shouting and waving guns at the hostages. I hoped that the negotiator was having some luck; it looked to me as though these guys weren't big on patience and were ready to start killing with the smallest amount of provocation.

Another twenty minutes passed, still we waited, the constant pressure of not knowing what may happen, along with the anticipation and the fear of entering another bloody battle was playing havoc with my psyche.

All of a sudden a shot was fired inside and a hostage slumped to the floor, I could hear the screams of the remaining hostages and the shouts of the rebels. Will Boato had told us that we would not be sent in unless he felt that he had to forfeit lives in order to get the rebels out of there. Now the guerrillas had started the murders and we would now have to try and minimise the carnage.

Another ten minutes passed, still we waited. Another shot and another dead hostage, more screams and more shouts of fear and despair. I guessed that the negotiator was making little or no progress. "Are they going to kill one hostage every ten minutes?" I wondered.

Finally, the call came through on the radio to move in. The decision had been made to get us to move in and save as many civilians as we could. This was something new for me, whenever I had done this before it had been training exercises, now there were real, innocent people's lives at stake (as well as my friend's lives, not to mention my own life too). I pushed the sense of dread to some far off place in my sensory system as I got on with what I'd been trained to do.

Moving closer, I could see a large man at the right hand side of the floor space; he was talking on a telephone, the handset propped on his shoulder with his head tilted to hold it in place. His hands were both full: a gun in one hand and a female hostage's hair in his other. He was shouting angrily down the phone and, as if to emphasise the point, was holding the gun to the side of the lady's head. An order came over the radio, a shot fired from some distance behind me crashing through the glass of the building and hitting the gunman full in the chest sending him spinning backwards as the sniper hit his target. We followed in with all guns blazing, and my heart racing to the extent that I could hear it above all the shooting and screaming, my chest feeling as tight as a tourniquet and my mouth as dry as the proverbial bone.

Two more hostages died as the rebels began to turn their weapons on the innocent as if to make the statement: "we may die, but we will take the hostages lives with us – so your rescue attempt has failed!"

Three more rebels were slain and two more had disappeared in the chaos leaving just the surviving hostages and members of our unit.

There were only a few doors off the main lounge area. Thankfully this was not Heathrow or J.F.K. otherwise we would have had a massive search on our hands.

Knowing that we had to find the two missing rebels, we split up. Billy and Joseph took the first door, Joe and I took the second, Michael and Benni took the third which left Juan and Jonathan to take the last. Louis and Paul led the remaining hostages to safety.

The door that Joe and I went through led in to what appeared to be an extremely long corridor. There were many more doors leading from it into a series of varying offices and rest areas.

"I was hoping for an empty fucking warehouse." I whispered smiling at the Swede.

"When have we ever been that farken lucky?" he grinned back.

We moved forward checking one door at a time; there was no sign of anybody in what was an edgy and uneasy search of the first five offices. Then, the sound of footsteps running for just a few steps came from further along the corridor. We looked at each other and signalled to move along swiftly, still checking as we went. We were not going to forget that there were two missing rebels waiting to shoot us on sight if we fucked up. Working with speed, we moved along the corridor until it came to a T-junction – we looked at each other with raised eyebrows. I signalled for Joe to stay at the junction and moved on to the left where there was just one open plan office in need of inspection for the missing men. Joe was positioned so that he could see in to the open plan office and also along the other branch of the corridor that was yet to be searched.

I moved in amongst the desks and office furniture, gun at the ready as I turned to look in each possible hiding space, working methodically. With adrenaline racing and my heart pounding like a bass drum through every inch of my body, I noticed a cloakroom area. It was full of coats and clothing with a set of lockers in a corner behind a partition. I signalled for Joe to join me, and once he had done so, I left him to watch my back.

Moving in to the cloakroom, I felt even more uneasy, but still working with the same care and attention, I worked along the rails towards the lockers at the rear.

Stopping a few metres from the set of lockers, I glanced back at the Swede, my intention was just to reiterate the real possibility that the missing man could be in there – it was a stupid mistake!

"Drop your weapon white boy!" came the voice, fear raced through me with the cold of the deepest winter. The rebel was holding an automatic pistol aiming straight at my chest - I dropped my gun.

"Good, now move back three steps and get down on your knees – you will be a good bargaining tool for my passage out of here." He nodded as I began to do as he said – my mind was racing, where the fuck was Joe? Had he seen what was going on? How do I get out of this shit-hole of a situation if the bastard with the gun stays out of my reach? I even thought how lucky I was that this guy had decided it was worth taking another hostage, rather than just blowing my brains out then and there. I was just kneeling there, my mind swimming, and staring at the man with the gun when I heard more footsteps coming towards me from behind.

I didn't get the chance to turn to see who it was that was behind me, as the gunman forced the end of the barrel into my forehead. I raised my hands to either side of my head and hoped like hell that he would not pull that trigger.

"I don't think that we'll be needing both of you..." he began. I wasn't about to hang on long enough for him to finish his sentence – if I was going to die, I was at least going to go out fighting! I had one chance and this was it! I exploded into action, bringing my hands forward, grabbing the gun barrel and forcing it up and away from my head. As soon as I made contact, the gun fired and the noise nearly deafened me as the bullet flew just over my head. Even though the shockwaves from the gunshot were still coursing through my veins, I didn't stop for a split second, continuing my grip on the gun (still forcing it backwards towards the gunman) I moved in to a standing position. His grip was lost as I kicked him hard in the balls, every ounce of the fear and adrenaline from that moment of shear terror travelling through my foot as the kick connected and I turned the gun on him as he lay on the floor. "Stay Down you cunt!" I told him (stamping hard on his face just to re-iterate the point). As I looked to see what was happening behind me, Joe was stood over the bleeding figure of the second missing rebel with his foot on his chest and that big stupid grin on his face. "Andy my man, you are really farken good – do you know that?" he said.

"And you are no fucking help – do you know that?" I asked him.

"That's not nice – the farker sneaked up on me!" he pleaded.

"That was what you were meant to be preventing, you big fucking turnip!" I informed him. As he started to argue his case, the cavalry in the form of Benni, Billy, Michael, Joseph, Jonathan and Juan came running in to find us as I tried to regain my composure.

"I thought that Mr Boato might be able to make an example of these bastards – what do you think guys?" I greeted them as cheerily as the nausea and horror of the moment allowed. My legs were trembling and bile rose in my throat as the reality of what had just taken place dawned on me.

The two captives were promptly and unceremoniously picked up and taken away by Benni, Jonathan and Juan.

I put my unsteady hand on the big Vikings shoulder, "come on Johan my man, I think we ought to get back to base and see if we can't get very, very drunk!" I told him.

CHAPTER TWELVE

Benni was getting married to Julietta. She was the daughter of a relatively wealthy hotel owner from Nabwana and they had been the archetypal childhood sweethearts, dating through High School and according to Benni, "completely in love!" I however, had no faith whatsoever in the notion of 'love' and was not about to start believing in it on Benni's say so. But, if there was to be a wedding, there would have to be a party and, whether Benni wanted one or not, a certain Viking and I were going to make sure there was a Stag Night!

The problem that we, as the (self appointed) Stag Party organisers had, was that nobody in Samawi seemed to understand the concept or reasoning of such an event. We however, were unwavering and did not let that deter us from such an important task.

The first obstacle to overcome was convincing Will Boato that he could do without the whole of our team for a full weekend. It took us a while, but having regaled him with stories from both English and Swedish Stag Parties (although I'd only ever actually attended one), he finally gave his permission for the necessary leave to be granted on the strict understanding that he was to be kept informed of details and, that he was also invited.

The rest of the guys in the team had taken little convincing of the necessity for such a congratulatory event and had agreed to help out in any way.

Paul, who was to act as the best man, had asked a thousand and one questions about the sort of thing that may go on at a Stag Night and had become so excited by the idea that at one stage we all thought that he might actually explode! Benni too had agreed that it was a great idea but was so busy with other arrangements for the big day that he had entrusted the organisation to us – the poor guy had actually believed that he had a choice in the matter!

A few weeks later, in a small twenty seater coach loaded with booze, driven by Noah (who was a cousin of Billy's that had agreed to the task of driving the Stag Party around after only a small amount of bribery) bound for the beauty of Calo, the Samawian Special Task Force and their Commanding Officer were off duty and determined to make the most of the weekend. I was doing my best to teach the lyrics of 'Blowing in the Wind' to the ignorant whilst strumming away at the battered old acoustic guitar that I'd gained from Marc and Suzi the Dutch travellers. It must have been an horrendous noise, eleven half pissed people singing only faintly in key to a song being poorly played on a guitar that was barely in tune. Every face on that coach was smiling and for what seemed like the first time ever, I saw those faces with no signs of angst, concentration or the usual uncertainties of a soldier's mind. The alcohol continued to flow as we made our way South with the entertainment not improving much as the guitar made it's way around various 'players' amongst us.

We arrived in Calo in what seemed to be a very short space of time and Noah stopped the coach outside a small hotel overlooking the bay where I had camped only a couple of months earlier. We'd booked all of the rooms on the first floor of the hotel for the weekend after Joseph had told us that he had stayed here with his wife when they had been to Calo to celebrate their first anniversary six months previously. Joe had pointed out that he may not be able to take her back again if the Stag Party was to be a rowdy affair.

As we all staggered slightly getting off the coach, I could see the concern on the faces of the hotel staff that had come outside to greet us. This was not helped by Paul, as stepping forward to shake the hand of the manager, he suddenly pulled his hand back towards his face and clenching his lips tightly shut, managed to actually vomit through his nostrils! The manager and maids looked horror stricken, I and everybody else in our group found it hilarious. Joe proceeded to slap the hapless Paul in between the shoulder blades which, I was sure, was not helping him to recover at all.

After our inauspicious arrival the hotel staff avoided us as much as possible, having been allocated our rooms, we were told that there was food available in the restaurant. Shortly afterwards, having devoured the buffet style lunch that was prepared for us (which served to soak up at least some of the alcohol consumed on our journey) Paul, (who after cleaning himself up and changing his vomit covered shirt) had eaten more than most of us and now looked a tad more human, suggested that we all go down to the beach for the afternoon. So, loaded with towels, bottles of various spirits, a football, a cassette player and plenty of heavy metal cassettes, we took ourselves down to the white sand and spent the afternoon playing five a side soccer, volleyball, racing up and down the sand dunes and swimming in the warm Atlantic water. Billy did try to challenge every one to a long jump competition but was promptly dragged by his feet along the beach and thrown fully clothed into the sea.

At night the hotel turned in to a lively venue full of people out to enjoy themselves. There was a dance hall that had been built on to the rear of the building and it appeared to be the hottest venue in town. Having all showered and changed after a sweaty afternoon on the beach, we sat down to a fabulous meal in the restaurant before moving on to the hammering noise and clammy atmosphere of the dance hall discotheque.

I spent most of the rest of that evening plying Benni with a myriad of cocktails and heavily spiked drinks. All of us spent most of the time on the dance floor mixing with the locals; everybody in the place seemed totally relaxed and at peace and – amazingly to me - there was not even a hint of any trouble of any kind.

As the DJ announced that he was playing the last tune of the night, as pre-arranged Joe, Billy, Michael and Joseph grabbed Benni and, carrying him above their heads took him outside the dance hall's main exit doors to a conveniently positioned street light. As they held him struggling vainly in their clutches, Jonathan and Louis whipped off his trousers and underwear while Juan and I grabbed his arms and proceeded to hand cuff him to the base of the aforementioned street light. Paul hovered on the outskirts of these goings-on looking slightly self-conscious and confused as to whether it was right for the best man to be involved in such an affair.

The last tune came to an end, and the hall started to empty; every single person that had been in attendance that night had to walk past the squirming and embarrassed figure of Benni in all his glory with genitalia on full view.

The local police constable arrived on the scene looking incredibly uncomfortable about the whole matter. He eventually approached the collection of sniggering fools that had put poor Benni in his predicament and asked the chuckling Will Boato which one of us was in possession of the key to the handcuffs.

"Ah!" I began, as the question was relayed to me, "that's where we may have a bit of a problem. Louis thinks he's lost the key!"

This only created more raucous, drunken laughter amongst us and added to the policeman's discomfort. "Please get your friend dressed and release him in whatever way you can!" he commanded before turning away and walking off with as much composure as he could muster.

"Has anybody got the fucking key?" I asked, and was met with varying degrees of negativity from more laughter to shrugs of the shoulders.

Joe however had decided on a more 'hands on' approach and had started rocking the lamppost. "It's not farken concreted in!" he shouted, "give me a hand guys?"

As I moved forward to help out, I glanced down at Benni, and nudging Billy who was now next to me I told him "I thought Benni was quiet".

Still stark bollock naked, the groom to be, was fast asleep amongst all the chaos and confusion.

Joe, Jonathan, Michael, Will and Joseph by now had the light at an angle of about forty-five degrees and were still rocking it back and forth. Benni stirred, smacked his lips, rolled over as much as the cuffs would allow and actually began to snore.

With even more laughter the street light was rocked, shaken and swayed until eventually all that was left in the ground were the wires that supplied it with electricity. Paul and Louis held Benni's shackled arms aloft while the rest of us somehow managed to thread the streetlight through in order to release him from his impromptu prison. With that, the drunken party finally came to an end as we split up and made our way back to our respective rooms.

The next morning at breakfast, all looking spectacularly the worse for wear, we sat looking at each other with smirks on our faces like a group of naughty school boys. We had apologised to the hotel manager for the damage to the lamppost and had clubbed together to pay for its repair. Will Boato, with typical efficiency, had found a spare key in his luggage and had freed Benni from his manacles. There was a great deal of piss taking during the buffet style breakfast, it had been a tremendous stag party and every one of us (even, or should that be 'especially', Benni) had thoroughly enjoyed ourselves.

Noah was not due to arrive at the hotel to pick us up until early that afternoon, so in an effort to sober ourselves up and shake the cobwebs of the hangovers away, we all set off for a walk to the beach.

We hadn't made it any further than the bottom of the hotel's front steps when the duty manager called us back "excuse me please, there is a telephone call for a Mr Boato"

We all looked at each other, immediately, as one, knowing that this had to be bad news. As Will went inside to take the call, the rest of us sat on the steps, none of us wanting to move until we had heard whatever news it was that Will was receiving in the phone call. I sat looking at

Benni with his head in his hands, trying to convince myself that we were mistaken; this could be nothing more than a trivial family matter for Will. When it came, the news couldn't have been much worse.

There had been another suicide bomb attack in Nabwana. It had been at the hotel that was owned by Julietta's father; the casualty list was huge, more than forty people had been injured. Fifteen guests had been killed in the bombing along with four members of staff including Julietta, her sister and her father.

Benni was inconsolable. All of us were devastated by the news, and being so far away in Calo, we all felt totally fucking useless. Noah was on his way, he had set out immediately on hearing news of the bombing and was due to arrive at least two hours ahead of schedule. When he did arrive, we threw the luggage on the coach and set off again straight away. It was good to be travelling back towards base where we could at least feel like we were able to do something practical; this was however, little comfort to the grief-stricken Benni.

The effect of that weekend stayed with us as a group for a long time after. Somehow, we were bonded even more closely than before – I put it down to a mixture of sharing the joy and celebration at the party and the collective anguish as we shared the grief of Benni for his beloved Julietta.

CHAPTER THIRTEEN

(December 1984)

It was Christmas Day, and at my parent's house the celebrations were in full swing. As had become the norm during my visits back home, I was pleased to see that my family were happy and healthy, but really didn't feel as though I truly belonged amongst them. The modern western Christmas was doing nothing to brighten my mood, as more and more presents were passed from family member to family member with no real appreciation being shown and no real tenderness being demonstrated from person to person, my mind drifted away to reflect upon the troubles of poor Benni and wonder how he was coping with his grief. It had only been two weeks since that terrible news was relayed to him and Benni had become very withdrawn and unusually distant from even his closest friends. Will Boato had told him to take as much time off as he felt he needed and Benni had been spending a fair amount of time with a counsellor. The whole of our unit had been present at the funeral service and I had been honoured that Benni had asked me to be one of the Pall Bearers for Julietta's coffin. It was an incredibly sombre day and if there had been a dry eye at that ceremony, I didn't notice it through my own tears.

I brought my mind back to England as the front door opened and my Grandparents walked in, cheerfully shouting Christmas greetings and bearing large bags full of gifts. My mood was brightened at the sight of my Nan and Gramps and I hurried across the room to greet them both with a colossal embrace. The day continued with the usual British customs of overeating, more gift swapping, petty squabbles over trivial matters such as what to watch on television and through it all, I watched from one corner or another hugging a bottle and feeling even more removed than ever before.

"The dog wouldn't mind a walk around the block." Gramps' voice broke through my doleful thoughts. I looked up to his smiling eyes and a knowing expression on his familiar face. "Yeah, I'd like that Gramps." I replied.

We walked for well over an hour with Gramps letting me talk, he was a terrific listener, only dropping in the occasional nugget of wisdom when I stopped and looked at him or asked him a direct question. By the time we got back to my Mum and Dad's house, my throat was dry from talking and 'Towser' my Grandparent's Jack Russell Terrier appeared to be worn out as he jumped on to the first vacant chair he could find and went straight to sleep.

Although the feeling of being an outsider in my own 'home' had not faded, my emotional state had lifted somewhat and I made more of an effort to join in with the rest of the day's festivities. It seemed quite bizarre for me to be doing something as uncomplicated and painless as playing Monopoly and Ker Plunk!

The next day, I joined the family on a walk around the local park before over eating again on leftovers from Christmas Day. Every body else seemed happy to slouch in front of the television or sleep it off for the rest of the afternoon, so I took myself off to visit Griff and his family while I had the chance. As I walked through the familiar streets where I had spent my childhood, the sense of not belonging returned to weigh my mindset down once more. This was not helped any by the three drunken men of about the same age as me, that came bursting out of an alley, beer cans in their hands nearly knocking me over. I side stepped them and shook my head before moving to carry on my way.

"Oi! Have you got a fucking problem mate?" Came the shout from behind me.

I didn't either want or need any trouble, so I carried on walking, hoping that the three other guys would do the same in the opposite direction. At the sound of running footsteps from behind me I knew that it wasn't going to be that simple.

I turned to see the three slowing as they reached me. "What's your fuckin' problem – you wanker!" said the nearest one to me; his mates were standing a little further back, not looking so eager for a fight.

"Easy mate." I told him "I don't want any trouble with you – why don't you go and enjoy your Christmas before you get hurt eh?"

For a second or two he was confused by my suggestion, but realising that he was losing face with his mates, he took a step forwards making a grab for me. I thrust my foot hard in to his knee as he did so, and saw the joint bend in the opposite direction to which it was designed for as he dropped like the proverbial sack of shit. He was screaming in absolute agony, rolling and writhing on the footpath, his mates looked horror-struck.

"You heard me fucking warn him – now pick him up and piss off!" I advised them, before carrying on my way to visit with my Ju Jitsu instructor and his family.

Griff looked happier than I'd ever seen him, being a father obviously suited him. We talked until late into the night, reminiscing over memories of training together and tournament triumphs and the laughter and tears that go with the ups and downs of taking any sport to the extreme.

On Griff's advice, first thing the following morning, I paid a visit to the local Police station to explain what had happened when I had met the three piss heads the previous evening. I was given a bit of a lecture by an aging Sergeant before being told that they had received statements from all three men at the hospital over night where the ringleader had been put in to plaster and his two friends had assured the Police that I had acted in self defence.

I spent the next week through to New Year mostly with my family and Grandparents, but visiting some old school friends too and generally trying to enjoy the socialising; but on January 2nd 1985 I was happy to be sitting on board an aeroplane bound, once again, for Samawi.

Arriving back at the base in Moyana, I was greeted by the smiling faces of Billy, Paul, Jonathan and Joe who had beaten me back by just two hours and didn't look like he had left at all. It was great to see my friends again, but the first thing from my mouth was, "how's Benni?"

Paul told me that he had seen Benni two days earlier and that he seemed to be a bit more like his old self; he was expecting to be back on duty in the next week or two.

The next day, back once again in the training hall at the base, Joe and I were scheduled to teach a group of newly assigned Military Policemen some knife defence. As the group filed in to the training area I was both surprised and pleased to see that amongst them were Isaac's brother and his cousin – they had come through the training and qualified as MP's.

It was a good day in many ways, although intrinsically what I was doing in Samawi was a job of work, I actually totally enjoyed every moment of it – and teaching that group of newly qualified military policemen that day, interacting with the big Swede to re-establish our 'double act' after our Christmas break, I actually felt far more at home than I had done for all of the ten days that I had just spent back in England.

CHAPTER FOURTEEN

Benni came back on duty two days before my twentieth birthday – the celebrations were kept low key out of respect for Benni. A bottle of twelve year old Glenlivet that had been a gift from my grandparents and an equally aged bottle of Laphroaig that Joe had presented me with in honour of the day were sunk by five of us (Joe, Billy, Michael, Joseph and myself) around a campfire on the beach while we sang along to the brilliance of Deep Purple, Led Zeppelin, Free and Iron Maiden blasting out of the cassette player.

A few days later, during a lunch break in the dining hall; Will Boato approached the table where Joe and I were discussing the plans for the afternoons training session with a group of new recruits. "Johan, Andy – I'd like you to meet Daniel Coelo, I'm placing him with you for the next three months – he's had a massive amount of combat experience which you will be able to benefit from and in return you will be able to help Danny with his fitness levels and knowledge of the methods that we've been developing – I think you guys will get along just fine!"

Looking at Danny, I took an instant liking to the man, he was no bigger than Billy, he looked wiry, I guessed that he was around ten years older than I was and he had an obvious jagged scar across his left cheek running from his eye to the edge of his mouth; which as I stood to shake his hand, broke into a broad smile as he spoke, "hey, how you doing man?" The voice really didn't fit with the man's appearance – it was like the DJ Emperor Roscoe had somehow got into Danny's voice box. A thought that as I got to know him better made more sense.

Danny had two days previous to our meeting been deported from the U.S.A. where he had spent the best part of two years in a prison in New Jersey for killing a man who had tried to rob him on the streets of New York. Danny had been on leave from the Samawian army's commando divisions and was visiting his half brother who had trained to be a Doctor in the states. Having flown in to New York that morning he was wandering around taking in the sites of the metropolis before finding the address of his relative. Danny at that time did not speak English and the unsuspecting robber had threatened him with a knife demanding money. All Danny had seen was a man waving a knife at him and had reacted in self defence, taking the knife off the robber and sticking it unceremoniously in his chest. Danny had been swiftly arrested, convicted and sentenced to life imprisonment. The Samawian government had managed to arrange for his deportation back to his homeland after long drawn out negotiations and after much ado within the government and the hierarchy of the military he was allowed back to his duties. (Danny had taught himself to speak English with the help of his American cellmate's radio whilst in prison – I had been pretty close with my initial guess of sounding like Emperor Roscoe!)

Over the following months, Danny became a fixture in the training hall alongside Joe and me. He trained hard, and as Will Boato had alluded to he struggled with his fitness at first, but after the initial period he was able to keep up with and hold his own with any of us. His fighting skills were excellent and as Joe and I were instructing the methods to groups we would often find Danny adding his thoughts and opinions, which were always relevant and we welcomed them.

In his time stationed with us Danny would join in with the training that Joe and I subjected our bodies to everyday – he would be with us for our morning runs and training on the beach (all of us pushing ourselves and each other to extremes) throughout the day. In the training hall he would observe, help or just join in with the students, he would spend meal times with us and would also join social get-togethers with our friends. He was a very experienced soldier and had been in many battles. Joe and I would talk through the emotional struggles that we had faced in our relatively small experiences and Danny would advise and encourage us both. He taught us a great deal about emotion control and how to operate under extreme pressures.

Eventually, the three months were up and Danny was moved to serve as an officer in a new regiment of Commandoes policing the rebel stronghold town of Cabilo – we never heard from him again, but he had made a massive mark on our lives.

Joe was twenty-one years old, I had been telling him for years that he was older, bigger, slower and uglier than I was, but, he had the right to a birthday celebration of some kind. Benni (who seemed to be becoming more like his old self again,) Paul and Jonathan had arranged for us all to go away on one of our climbing and skydiving weekends on Mount Nabinda and over the Great Nomali River. All of our unit was going and packed ready with a crate of 'Dragon's Breath' kindly donated by Michael and Joseph we made our way to the helicopter that had been commandeered for the occasion. Louis, Juan and Billy had loaded three huge crates of food onto the aircraft alongside the tents, parachutes and other equipment needed for the trip.

As I climbed on board ahead of the big Swede, there was a massive explosion from the other side of the base. We all knew that the weekend's revelry would have to be postponed as the sound of gunfire followed the initial blast as the guerrilla militia attacked the base again.

As one, the team made our way to our 'control room', contacted Will Boato to tell him that we were on our way, and armed ourselves before making our way towards the area of attack. The scene was an eerily familiar one – it had been over two years since my first experience of this kind – and the same office block was under mortar fire. There were small groups of our soldiers dotted around the courtyard firing sporadically at the rebels who had started to move in towards the base. The initial blast that we had heard had blown the gates and half of the wall down on the other side of the yard. Will Boato had come to meet us and told us that he had enough men to hold the rebels where they were at the moment, but he had no idea how many there were on the outside of the walls and where they were situated – that was our job.

"Happy Birthday Bro'!" I slapped the Viking on the shoulder as we moved out in two groups on either side at the rear of the chaotic yard. I was with Michael, Billy, Benni and the Swede as we scrambled unnoticed in to a small group of trees overlooking the battleground to assess the situation. Michael was in radio contact with Joseph who, with the rest of the unit were situated somewhere on the other side of the guerrilla's attacking force. I lay next to Benni looking out at the commotion below us, just a short distance away to our left the sight of a small cloud of smoke rising above a wall caught my eye and I nudged my friend. Benni looked to where I was pointing as we both realised where the mortars were being fired from. I rolled over to tell Michael and the others what I'd seen as Benni burst from the cover running down hill towards the wall. This was crazy, from where we were we couldn't see behind the wall, we didn't know how many rebels there were with the mortar launchers and we hadn't had time to complete a full 'reccy' of the surrounding area. But, Benni was running full tilt towards where the mortars were being fired from. Michael immediately called Joseph on the radio. Joseph had seen Benni and could see the surrounding ground from his position; it was clear. At once, I set off after Benni, quickly followed by Joe, Billy and Michael. As we reached the wall, Benni was sprinting around it, Kalashnikov held at waist height firing like a madman at whatever was awaiting him on the other side of that wall. Joe stood against the wall and hooked his hands together to give me a foot hold as I launched myself up to the top of the structure, beside me Billy was doing the same aided by Michael. As we hit the top of the wall we set ourselves, guns at the ready, to help the crazed Benni in any way we could. There were nine rebels behind that wall; they had been alerted by Benni's demented screams as he ran towards them gun blazing. He had killed three of them before he was almost cut in half by the bullets ripping into his torso. Joe and Michael were now on the wall with us and we were able to eliminate the rest of that group of guerrilla militia men. I couldn't see any more than the shape of my rebel targets through the tears in my eyes as the body of my friend lay shot to pieces on the ground below me.

The battle faded and the guerrillas once again were defeated. In the late afternoon, as a unit, we sat under the fruit trees by the small pool, none of us wanting to separate the remaining number of our team. Each of us silent with our own thoughts and emotions remembering Benni – who it seemed through his berserk deed, was once again with his beloved Julietta. Eventually, as darkness descended, with wordless gestures of solidarity, we broke up and went back to our rooms for what was for me one of the longest, sleepless, disturbed nights that I have ever endured.

Two days later, on the day that we should have been sky diving over the beautiful Nomali River, we sat on the beach once again, and with the same low key celebrations as had befit my own birthday, we wished Joe a "Happy twenty first birthday!"

CHAPTER FIFTEEN

(June 1985)

The darkness enveloped me. I'd been sat in the same position for well over an hour in a supposedly disused warehouse in Nabwana. Our intelligence suggested that guerrilla militia were operating from the site, and that there was to be a meeting of some of the rebel leaders. Our task was to interrupt the meeting and to do some serious damage to the guerrilla militia by taking out the 'top brass'.

Also at varying points of the building in varying degrees of discomfort, were Joe, Michael, Joseph, Billy, Jonathan, Paul and Louis. Juan had dislocated his shoulder in a training session about a week earlier when I had thrown him with a bit too much force causing him to land awkwardly. This hadn't stopped me ribbing him about having "any excuse to pull out of a bit of action!"

So, we waited in the shadows of the gloomy building for a sign of the promised meeting. After another hour the roller shutter door to the west of the building finally jolted me to attention. As two Mercedes, one black, one silver drove in to the warehouse followed by a dark blue Range Rover, I slowly shifted my position to allow for a clear view as the lights of the vehicles pierced the gloom. The cars were all parked facing each other in a triangular fashion, with the lights left on. Four men jumped out of the Range Rover and another four from the black Mercedes, a further three from the silver car. The man who had been closing the roller door quickly joined them and they all positioned themselves around the outside of the triangle. Once this was done, one more man climbed out of each vehicle and went to the inside of where the cars were parked to greet each other. These were obviously the top men, it was an incredible scene, the sort of event that takes place in gangster movies when there's a deal going down with the mafia bosses. Now the movie was being acted out in front of my eyes and I was about to 'enter stage left' to play my part.

We all knew what had to be done; the most important part of this mission was to kill the three men in the centre of the meeting. The supporting cast of the rebels on the outside were secondary to the proceedings. But, as soon as we made any kind of move, the three targets would be wrapped up in a protective huddle and our task would become more complex. As the usual mix of luck and judgement would have it, we had chosen our relative positions well. With the better gunmen of Michael, Jonathan and Louis perched in the rafters to act as snipers for the initial killings, the rest of us were to open fire on the other rebels to stop them picking off the guys above whose positions would be obvious as soon as they started firing. We would also have to deal with any close quarter combat that was necessary.

I waited, trying to control my breathing, my heart racing with that now familiar adrenalin pump. The opening shots rang out and I instinctively reacted to play out my role in the lethal scene. I saw the three leaders fall as I aimed my own weapon at the closest confused and terrified man to me, killing him instantly in his bewilderment, I moved my aim to the next man who fell in the same vein. It was all over within a couple of minutes, fifteen rebel lives taken, hardly a shot fired in retaliation. We began to move out of the building to make our escape, but were halted in our tracks by the sound of a truck pulling up outside the roller doors. We reversed our movements and disappeared in to the shadows at the other end of the warehouse.

The doors opened and twelve men walked through for only a few metres before stopping aghast at the sight that met them. Shouts rang out and more men came running in to the building. In the darkness, I managed to find a door and by sheer chance the key was hanging on a nail on the doorframe. With the ensuing chaos going on in the building we filed out of the back door as the rebels searched the building for the killers of their leaders.

We split in to pairs as we left the warehouse; we expected there to be search parties of guerrillas – they might have been murderous bastards, but they were extremely well organised murderous bastards. The actual assassination aspect of the mission had been too easy; if we were to run true to form, I knew that things would have to get much shittier before they got better again.

Joe and I ran to the far end of the empty car park at the rear end of the warehouse. We had a rendezvous point a mile and a half from the building where we were to meet the rest of the team at a safe house before moving back to base. Climbing over the chain link fence, staying in the shadows we made our way along an alley. We could hear shouts from the rebels all around us as the searching groups thought they'd seen somebody. I hoped that they were wrong and that all our guys were safe. As we moved along, at the far end of the alley in the direction we needed to go I saw three men approaching us. There was no way that we could have shot at them without raising alarm and if we retraced our steps we would have no doubt encountered even more searching groups. We stayed where we were, both of us intuitively knowing what the other was thinking, staying in the shadows on either side of the alley as the three men moved nearer to us. As they reached us, Joe grabbing the nearest man by covering his mouth with his hand, cut the rebel's throat in a split second before stabbing a second rebel in the heart. I watched the big Swede swiftly going through those actions as I held a thrashing rebel's neck in a silent stranglehold, feeling him die second by second as my arm cut off the blood supply to his brain.

We moved on to the end and out of the alley, and staying in the shadows as much as possible almost ran headfirst into another group of three rebels. As we skidded to a halt, the first man saw me and with a backhanded slashing motion brought a knife down towards my neck. I moved behind the knife arm, blocking the stab and bringing my elbow crashing into his face. On doing so, moving closer to him, I broke his arm across my chest as a second man ran at me with his knife aimed at my stomach. I just managed to move out of his way before throwing my forearm into his throat crushing his windpipe with his momentum meeting my body motion. Joe had taken out the third man in the group with his usual deadly efficiency. The guy with the crushed windpipe was making a hell of a raspy, rattling sound, so, as we moved away I silenced him by bringing my foot down hard on his temple.

We made our way to the safe house without any further aggravation; Billy and Jonathan were already there, Louis and Paul following just two minutes after our arrival. It was another two hours before Michael and Joseph turned up – Joseph had received a nasty stab wound to his left shoulder and after losing a vast amount of blood had had to be virtually carried by Michael from just outside the warehouse.

With all things considered, we had achieved our goal and made a real mess of the guerrilla militia's hierarchy. They would have to go through a fair amount of re-organisation - and by the nature of the beast there was always a great deal of infighting within rebel forces – so despite the fairly messy nature of the task we had just undertaken and the serious injury to Joseph, we deemed the mission to be a relative success as we drove back to Moyana to the base. After depositing Joseph in the safety of the military hospital, Michael found another supply of 'Dragon's Breath' to toast another safe return. At ninety percent proof, the evil liquid was even more dangerous than the rebel militia – but joined by Juan, we drank to Joseph's health and 'absent friends' as we talked through and even laughed about the events of the day. All in all, things could have been a hell of a lot worse, we had come out of the mission virtually unscathed and Joe and I were due to go on leave in two days time.

The following morning, with more than one manner of hangover, we had a debriefing with Will Boato who informed us that the neighbouring Republic of Cobolo had been mustering its forces on the border and was known to be preparing to invade the disputed borderlands between the two countries.

The big Swede and I were told that we could have the allocated two weeks leave but if things had not dramatically changed when we returned, we would probably be on 'code red' (under emergency instructions) for some time to come.

CHAPTER SIXTEEN

Joe had only ever visited England once as a child when his parents had taken him to see the traditional tourist sights of London. His father, a music journalist, had been reporting on a T-Rex concert and had used the opportunity to take his family on a sightseeing trip for the weekend.

Now, with two weeks leave, we had decided to create a complete change of pace and fly to the U.K., hitch-hike to Cumbria in order to disappear into the wilds of the Lake District. With tents on our backs and an adventurous yet peaceful state of mind we arrived in a drizzly Ambleside with no more than my childhood holiday memories to give us directions.

After buying some Kendal Mint Cake and a local walking guide from one of the many 'gear shops' in the small town, we made up our minds to just go into the hills and get back to nature for a day or two. So, after buying the essentials of a camping stove and gas, saucepan, frying pan, bread and butter, rice, tins of beans, bacon, eggs, sausages, flapjacks and a bottle of Glenfiddich we set off. Walking through the park behind the church, heading to the hills, we stopped and looked at each other. With the English summer rain continuing to fall and stick our waterproof jackets to our bodies and our hair to our faces, we must have looked like any of the thousands of rambling visitors that descend upon that part of the world every year, but to us the sense of doing something that didn't involve any pressure, and had an element of childish fun about it suddenly hit us both at the same time. Standing on a footbridge over a small, trickling river, as groups of ramblers and couples walked by, we exploded with raucous laughter as the exhilaration and amusement of doing something for no reason hit us for the first time in far too long.

We made our way along the route that was given to us by the purchased paper guide and, after climbing up steep footpaths, soon found ourselves on the rugged slopes of Loughrigg fell. As if to greet us, the rain had ceased, the clouds had burnt away and we were now walking in the Cumbrian sunshine and being treated to some beautiful scenery. The gnarled and tough-looking Langdale Pikes, the delightful and stunning views over Lake Windermere left us amazed and all the troubles of Samawi were driven to the backs of our minds as we acted like kids competing with each other, racing up and down slopes, climbing trees and throwing stones.

We set up camp in a copse as dusk began to fall, we ate sausages and beans, drank water from a mountain stream along with the scotch and watched the local wildlife of rabbits, owls and red squirrels look at us with astonishment, wondering what the hell we were doing on their turf.

The next morning, we packed the equipment onto our backs again and carried on our way; the scenery became even more beautiful. There were picturesque, lily covered tarns looking like Constable had painted them, or were fresh out of a Jane Austen story. Forests of conifer trees spread over complete mountainsides, our path took us to the top of a rocky mountain slope where we sat and ate the flapjacks as we wondered at the views over Grasmere, Rydal and the fabulous countryside beyond.

Wandering through the same fields as Wordsworth had once walked; we found ourselves once again back in Ambleside. We lunched at a pub called the Queens Head and on the advice of the barman there, set off once again to make our way along the mountain road known as the Kirkstone Pass. Kirkstone Pass runs from Lake Windermere over and through mountains and eventually comes to the lake of Ullswater at Glenridding. The weather was still being kind to us as we made our way along the narrow road leading from the town to meet the main Kirkstone pass. We had purchased a local Ordnance Survey map from a gear shop and had been told to take the route known locally as 'The Struggle'. Walking up the extremely steep road it was obvious where the name came from. We finally managed our way to the Pass road, meeting it at an aging pub simply called the Kirkstone Inn as the sun disappeared behind an ominous looking black cloud that was coming in from behind the mountains. We decided to walk on up into the mountain overlooking the inn where the sun was still shining on the stony ridge. We raced up to the summit to be greeted by a disused slate quarry on one side and mind-blowing views along the road towards Glenridding on the other. The landscape was incredible as we walked along the mountaintops, until setting up camp against the negligible shelter of a pile of stones as dusk and the inevitable rain began to fall.

The cold and heavy rain on that English mountainside did nothing to dampen our spirits – for two young men who had been subjected (through their own decisions it must be said) to extreme violence and dreadful pressures for the previous three years without any real let up, these few days of trekking without a recognisable plan of action, was peace and tranquillity itself.

Morning came and the night's rain eased, the morning sun burnt the remaining cloud away and we set off again in glorious sunshine. Over the next few days we camped at the side of the beautiful lake of Brotherswater which is surrounded by mountains on all sides. We watched badgers play as we fed them peanuts and stale bread. We followed the pass through Patterdale to Glenridding and hiked up and over the strenuous ridge of Striding Edge before spending the night camped at the summit of Helvellyn. It felt incredibly cold up there to a couple of guys who had become accustomed to the African heat, but as dawn broke and the morning sun shone on the mountain we packed up once more and raced each other down the rocky Swirral Edge on the other side of the mountain, to jump naked in to Red Tarn – this was our first attempt at anything resembling a wash in five days. The icy cold water made us scream out loud and our cries disturbed a group of four students from Nottingham who had been camping behind stones about ten metres from where we had abandoned our clothes – two trained 'Special Forces' soldiers had not noticed their bright orange tents before running stark bollock naked in to the freezing water!

After an extremely embarrassing first few minutes of introduction, explaining that Joe was from Sweden and that we were merely following traditional Scandinavian customs, the male students gave their names as Scott and Alex; their red-faced girlfriends were introduced as Alison and Mandy. They had been hiking in a similar fashion (without the brazen nudity) for a week and were heading back to University that evening. They cooked us a mighty breakfast of bacon, eggs, beans, sausages and mushrooms with rich, strong coffee and welcomed us in to their group as if we were long lost friends. We walked with them back down the mountain and into Glenridding where we hired motorboats and raced each other around the islands of Ullswater, much to the annoyance of the serious sailors in the dinghies and the cruise boat operators - the shouts of disdain merely added to our amusement.

After terrorising the middle aged, middle classes in their toys for an hour or two, Scott informed us that the next day was his twenty first birthday and that his parents owned a pub in Nottingham where they were putting a big party on for him. He invited us along, saying that it would be great if Joe and I would go along for the celebrations. After only a small amount of consideration we agreed and soon found ourselves crammed in to the back of Alison's Ford Escort estate along with all of the camping equipment on the road to Nottingham.

The party was a crazy affair with the two of us being introduced to lots of people that we would never see again after that evening, but every one of them making us feel welcome. We had a fabulous, drunken time, partying with everybody as though we had known them forever.

The next morning we said our goodbyes and hitch hiked back to Birmingham, where, after arranging to meet each other at Nabwana airport, Joe got a flight to Stockholm to visit his parents for a few days and I went to see my family with the usual trepidation and unease.

There was indeed the usual awkwardness about my visit at my parent's house, but it was good to see them in relatively good health and spirits. My Grandparents were delighted to see me and my Nan fed me with as much food as I could handle without actually bursting at the stomach.

The morning of my flight back to Africa came, and after kissing my family goodbye once more, I sat in the lounge at Birmingham airport waiting for the call to board, wondering to what news I would be flying back. I was still not, and never would be, officially a Samawian soldier. I did not have to go back at all. I was still, after all, just a guest, a bizarre thought with all the shit that I had put myself through for my friends and the unit. If I had had the opportunity to do it all again, I would have done everything in exactly the same way. There was nothing on earth that was capable of making me miss that flight to get back to Samawi, my friends in the unit and the life that I had become accustomed to.

CHAPTER SEVENTEEN

I met Joe at the manager's office of Nabwana airport as had been pre-arranged back in England. We drove back to the base town of Moyana in my Land Rover, which had been left at the airport, talking through the hiking trip in Cumbria and listening to Led Zeppelin on the stereo. Both of us were really wondering what the news would be when we got back, but holding on to the peace of the moment on the journey.

As soon as we arrived back at the base, we unpacked as quickly as possible and went to find Will Boato.

On our way to his office we met Billy, who told us that the news was as bad as could be expected. The neighbouring Republic of Cobolo were no longer responding to dialogue or listening to reason over the disputed borders despite every effort from the Samawian government. Their forces had a few days earlier sent tanks in to the border lands of Samawi and taken control of the region, creating refugees out of the families which had been living in the area and murdering in cold blood those who were brave enough to try and stay in their homes.

Michael, Joseph, Jonathan, Louis and Paul were already in the borderland gathering whatever information that they could. Billy, the newly healed Juan, Joe and I were going to travel to meet them in the Northern town of Gabale the following day.

As Billy finished telling us this news, Juan appeared and told us that Will had heard that we were back on the base and that he had sent Juan to fetch us along with Billy to his office. Once there, Will told us the exact same information that Billy had given already, adding that he had heard from Michael and the others. They had managed to find out the identification and whereabouts of the commanding officers behind the invasion. We were to fly up to Gabele to meet with the rest of them with our mission being to find a way in to the enemy HQ and eliminate the commander of the invading problem forces.

That evening, the four of us were looking at maps of the problem area; it soon became apparent that this was going to be even more problematic than it had at first sounded. The region was very mountainous (making the English Lake District seem just a little hilly) but, to add to the difficulty, on either side of the mountains, the land was incredibly flat and barren to the point of being desert on the Cobolan side.

The next morning, loading the now familiar helicopter with as much equipment, ammunition and weaponry as we could physically carry without being hampered, we flew up to Gabele to the predetermined rendezvous point. After greeting the rest of our team and catching up with the obligatory insults and mockery, we ate lunch and ran through the options open to us for the mission in hand – there were not many, it was going to be delicate, tricky and not far from fucking unworkable!

The only way to get into Cobolo undetected was via the mountains. The passes were all heavily guarded during the day and still guarded, just not so heavily, after dark. The temporary military base that the invasion was being commanded from was five miles from the mountains across the deserted wastelands and was obviously very fucking fortified and guarded at all times. We knew that the Commander-in-Chief was going to be camped there that night, so, true to form, it was a 'now or never' situation for the Samawian Special Task Force.

Sky diving out of a helicopter is, to say the least, tricky at the best of times. The same can be said for sky diving to land on rocky, hilly terrain. To parachute at night out of a helicopter on to rock-strewn mountains is sheer fucking madness, but nine of us did it and got away with no more than a few grazes and bruises to show for our suicidal jumps.

We gathered the parachutes and packs together and in true James Bond fashion stashed them away at the back of a handy cave that was found after just a few minutes of searching. About two hundred metres down hill we encountered our first guards, two guys sat smoking marijuana on a fallen boulder, Jonathan and Louis took them out, and carried them back up the hill to sleep forever on the 'chute' packs.

We made good progress for a while after that and travelled uninterrupted across the ground from the mountains until we were within a mile of the temporary Cobolan base. On the newly worn hard mud road between the mountain range and the base there was a 'check point' of a port-a-cabin occupied by three guys in uniform playing cards and smoking (probably marijuana – we didn't get close enough to smell the stuff). There were rolls of barbed wire in 'Great Escape' fashion for about a hundred metres either side of the 'check point'. We walked around unnoticed and moved on towards the base.

"Do you think there is any chance it can carry on being this farken easy?" the big Swede whispered to me. "Not a fucking chance!" I told him.

At the Cobolan base, it was all quiet. They were not likely to be expecting an invasion and, if any attack was going to happen they'd have expected thousands of guys in tanks and all sorts of armoured shit – definitely not a meagre nine lunatics with a communal death wish.

The information regarding the temporary base had come from a captured Cobolan soldier along with the surveillance work that Michael and the guys had been getting up to while Joe and I were playing on the Cumbrian Mountains. The next part of our mission was reliant upon the Cobolan man's given information. As we approached the fences, I hoped that his interrogation had been a competent and proficient one.

The cabin that we needed to get into could be seen from the outside of the six-foot double chain-link fence as we gathered there. Much to our amazement there were no guards about at this point and we were hidden from view by a group of trucks and personnel carriers that had been parked by the barrier.

As Paul and Billy cut a hole in the fence, I went through the plan in my mind trying to visualise it all going without a hitch. Joe nudged me and signalled for us to go. Leaving Paul and Billy at the fence, the rest of us moved in to the enemy camp staying in the darkness and the shadows of the conveniently parked vehicles we made good progress at first. Then, suddenly four soldiers moved from behind a truck and walked straight towards the hole in the fence, they couldn't have heard anything as there was no urgency about their movements but if they had got any closer we would have been in the shit. Signalling to the first three of my friends that I could make out in the darkness, we all moved as one; the four Cobolans were silently taken out and their bodies hidden under a truck in the gloom.

Leaving three more of our team, Louis, Joseph and Juan at a convenient point to watch our backs and if need be 'make safe' our exit, I moved on with Michael, Jonathan and the Viking. We moved cautiously, my heart pounding as we made it to the Officer's cabins. There were lights on inside, from where we could hear voices of men talking. We knew that, once inside the building, all hell would let loose and we would have to be in and out in as short a time as possible. The longer we were in there the more chance there was of the mission failing, and us not making it back.

Michael and Jonathan moved to the rear of the cabins, I signalled for Joe to follow me in the front door. Pulling knives from their sheaths (we were only to use guns as a last resort) we moved in. I opened the door slowly to be greeted by a shocked tall man with a moustache that made him look like the cartoon character Yosemite Sam. He didn't stay shocked for too long, he lunged to grab me and I killed him within a second, the life flowing out of him through his sliced throat.

Joe had silenced another by breaking his neck and we moved across the room. A door opened as I was passing it, and three more men entered the room. The last one did not get very far as I put him to sleep, grabbing him from behind and stopping his circulation. Joe managed to cut another one down, but I was a split second too slow getting to the third and he threw a kick that caught me on the thigh. I knew that he had to be silenced and moved in taking another blow from his fist on my forehead as I hurried to quieten him. He was just starting to cry out as I crushed his voice box with the arc of my hand.

The stifled scream had been enough to raise alarm amongst the other officers in the cabins. The first person in to the room, however, was Michael quickly followed by Jonathan. "Go, go, go!" shouted Michael as he raced towards the far door. Gunfire started from outside and behind us. We made it out of the cabin and un-slinging weapons from our backs as we ran, under the cover of the fire of our three friends; we got across to the cover of the parked vehicles. It seemed as though everything had gone to shit, we would be lucky to get away now and we didn't even know if we had taken out the targeted Officer. We made it through the fence and ran as a group across the barren countryside in the pre-planned opposite direction to the way we had gone in. Billy was screaming into a radio as we ran.

"Did you find him?" I asked Michael as we ran – he looked at me quizzically, "Did you get the top man?"

"You did Andy," he said, "big man, big moustache. Either you or Joe got him; I saw his body as we ran out of there!"

I couldn't believe what he was telling me, the very first person that we had encountered had been the Commander-in-Chief. I had killed the guy within a second of going in there, we could have just turned around and run out of the base and nobody would have known about it until we were back in Samawi.

As it was we were being pursued by half of the Cobolan army and we were still a good Kilometre from our rendezvous.

As that thought went through my head, the familiar sound of the twin blade helicopter came from the darkness above. Billy screamed into his radio again and a search light piercing the darkness shone from the sky fifty metres to our left. With gunfire and voices echoing behind us, we ran with all the speed we could muster, to meet the aircraft that had come to rescue us from a certain death.

The helicopter dropped us back in Gabale and after taking some time to compose ourselves again, eat a hard-earned meal and talk through the events of the night, we commandeered a driver and an army truck to take us back to our base in Moyana. Michael had somehow, once again managed to find a supply of the evil liquid that we had come to call 'Dragon's Breath' and we drank in the back of the truck as we travelled back to base. We had risked even more considerable danger than we had before – with the parachute jump alone, our lives had been on the line. Breaking into the Cobolan base had been a genuine 'suicide mission' and to get out unscathed after all of the hand to hand combat and being shot at by the Cobolans was something worth celebrating. Like a bunch of fools we were fucking around in the back of the truck with the sheer relief washing over us. After all of that danger and death, the perfect irony happened to a long haired young Englishman – I was swinging on the frame at the back of the vehicle, larking around, when the sweat on my hands caused me to lose grip on the rail. I fell off the back of the truck, landing on the road, wrecking my back and putting myself out of action for six weeks!

CHAPTER EIGHTEEN

(September 1985)

The weeks of being bed-ridden had felt like a prison stretch to me. I had been active for the whole of my life, right from the moment that I could walk; to be confined to bed and flat on my back for over a month was like torture. I had been extremely fucking bad tempered and irritable – the nurses, doctors and physiotherapists all told me that I was almost certainly the worst patient in the world – which was probably as much down to my embarrassment over the manner of the accident as much as the excruciating pain shooting through every sinew in my body. It certainly was no reflection on the ability and expertise of the staff, as they were unbelievably talented and I was up and about and had started gentle exercises after only forty days.

The rest of the unit had visited as often as they could during my confinement, and they all had a great laugh at my expense. On the day that I returned to my room at the base, there was a small trampoline wrapped up as a gift, with a harness attached to it with climber's karabiners and a note from the guys in the unit recommending that I was to keep it strapped to my back on future missions.

Things in the borderlands had quietened down for a few weeks after our night time operation. But, over the week or two leading up to my return to duty, there had been intelligence and confirmation of small troops of Cobolan soldiers invading Samawian villages in the region and carrying out mass murders of the inhabitants including women and children.

It was good however, after only a few days of gentle 'rehab' workouts, to feel fully fit once more and get together with the guys in the training hall for a combat session. Whether it was the enforced rest that had benefited my conditioning or reaction time, or if it was purely my eagerness to get back into it, I will never know, but during that day's training, I seemed to feel better than I had ever felt before. Even though as a team we always pushed each other and ourselves to real extremes, I welcomed every test and trial of the day and pressed every body to work to extremities that even we hadn't reached before in practice.

A week after returning to duty, I was back in Gabale with the rest of the Samawian Special Task Force. Our intelligence unit had calculated a proposed pattern that the Cobolan 'murder squads' would be working to, and it was our mission to move into the Borderlands, find this brutal troop and eliminate them before they could inflict another massacre upon the Samawian population.

After three days operating under the guidelines of the Intelligence Unit's strategy, trying to sleep in any kind of cover in soaring daytime temperatures and travelling in the cold of night, moving from village to village, on foot and as secretly as possible, we were beginning to have our doubts regarding the intellect of our Intelligence Unit.

Then, as seven of us stopped to drink some water and check routes, Billy and Louis, who had been taking their turn at scouting ahead of the group, returned to report that they had sighted a troop of Cobolans less than two kilometres from where we were. This had to be them. We listened to what Billy and Louis had seen and made our plan of attack. The Cobolan troop was camped and inactive, but it seemed that they were all awake. This made sense as all reports of their attacks on villages suggested that they had been at sunrise. Intelligence reports said that the Cobolan troop numbered about twenty soldiers and it seemed that what Billy and Louis had seen backed this up. This was obviously a group of cruel and merciless men who had no qualms about killing in cold blood, whether it were men, women or babies. They had demonstrated this too many times already and it was our job to put a stop to there murderous campaign. The one thing that we had to do above all others however, was to not let those thoughts cloud our judgment – we had to keep our emotions within and treat this in the same manner as any other mission.

We made our way to the Cobolans camp and having split into groups of three, surrounded the area to cover all angles. With me, were the usual big Viking and Jonathan. Billy, Michael and Joseph were another set; leaving Paul, Louis and Juan – as had worked so many times for us before. The better gunmen of Michael, Jonathan and Louis were to stay back to pick off the Cobolan soldiers and cover any crap that may occur (including shooting any fleeing Cobolans) while the rest of us moved in to the camp at varying angles to engage and eradicate the murderous troop at close quarters.

We moved in under the shadows of the tents with the unsuspecting enemy all around. Joe was behind me as we ran silently from the cover of a tent to a position close to a group of four soldiers stood talking by a truck. I began to signal my intention to the big Swede when from the opposite side of the camp I heard a yell and chaos ensued.

The four soldiers turned to look towards the yell, two shots rang out as Joe and I ran forwards to attack the four men. We hit them hard and fast and two men died instantly as our knives were embedded in them. The man that I had hit fell awkwardly taking me to the ground with him and causing me to lose my knife. As I started to get up again a boot caught me full force in the side of the rib cage and I rolled in the dirt with the wind forced out of me. The owner of the boot followed me with the intention of causing more pain, but he made the mistake of moving in too closely and I punched him in the balls with as much force as I could muster. As I began to stand to finish the fucker off, I was grabbed from behind in a stranglehold by another man screaming down my ear for his mate to kill me. I was losing consciousness fast now. As the man with the sore groin came at me with a blade aimed at my throat, I kicked out as hard as I could at his knee. Thankfully, the kick struck home, he stopped and dropped to the floor allowing me to concentrate on escaping from the man strangling me – gathering all of my remaining energy, I threw my elbows back in to his stomach and grabbing his wrist threw myself to the floor throwing him over my shoulder to land on top of his mate with the knife. Joe was moving towards me with blood coming from his head but a smile on his face and the camp was becoming quieter. As I turned to speak to my friend, another Cobolan ran screaming from a nearby tent with a machete aimed at my head. Before I could react he was almost upon me. Dropping low, I blocked the arm that was wielding the blade as I smashed my forearm into his groin. Feeling him slump, I grabbed his leg with the arm that had hit his balls and as I stood upright again, I took him to the floor, stamping hard on his head as he landed.

As I looked up again I saw the rest of our team finishing the task at hand making prisoners of any surviving Cobolans and calling in the waiting Samawian soldiers to take them away for questioning etc.

Returning once again to base on the evening of the following day, with a few of us patched up including Joe with seven stitches in a head wound, Paul with a broken nose and Juan with twelve stitches in his left forearm (not to mention my seriously sore ribs and neck). The unmarried amongst us which included me along with Joe, Jonathan, Juan and Louis, sat around the ubiquitous camp fire on the beach talking and laughing as Joe and I tried to teach the other three friends the lyrics to Deep Purple's 'Child in Time' and we all failed miserably as we attempted to sing the high notes in the style of Ian Gillan.

CHAPTER NINETEEN

(November 1985)

As things calmed down enough between Samawi and the Republic of Cobolo, the regular Army Units began to handle most of the fighting which had basically fallen in to a series of 'tit for tat' retaliatory strikes. The guerrilla militia had continued to operate in a minimal fashion. The usual vein of bomb strikes and hostage taking had become rare, but the underlying threat was still extremely serious and the rebel forces were known to be continually recruiting new members. Consequently, the regular forces and the Intelligence Units were kept extremely busy, while the Samawian Special Task Force got on with their individual 'off duty' duties. This for me, was to be running the Combat Instruction at the base along with Joe and due to the recruitment drive and continually rising influx of new conscripts, Billy and Juan were also helping with the day to day running of the instruction programme. Michael, Jonathan and Louis were firearms instructors whilst Joseph and Paul were now instructors with the parachute regiment.

Nevertheless, we always met up for our own regular training and saw each other socially at least once a week.

This usually meant getting terribly intoxicated on the beach and singing dreadful renditions of excellent songs!

On a night out away from the beach, at a bar in Moyana, Juan met a young nurse called Kara. They immediately began to spend every spare second that they had together and within weeks it became obvious that they were completely head over heels in love with each other.

The problems began when Juan started turning up late for the early morning starts in the training hall with his allocated students. Kara worked at the nearby military hospital and had an allocated flat there and Juan had all but moved in. The flat was no more than three kilometres from the base, but Juan had been used to living in his digs on the base and had become conditioned to being able to 'fall out of bed and in to the training hall'.

After the first couple of days of this happening we had given Juan a lot of verbal stick and hoped that he would get his act together by turning up on time each morning – he didn't, so we had to resort to more tangible and agonizing methods of getting the message across.

With the approval and help of Billy and Joe, we designed a new plan and itinerary for the training programmes so that the four of us would be instructing all of the groups together each morning. Juan would not however be leading any of the instruction but simply assisting either me, Joe or Billy. We planned to use him as a 'stooge' to help us demonstrate each technique that we would be teaching until things got so painful for him that he could no longer 'oversleep' in the mornings!

On the first day we had a large group of new recruits in to learn basic striking and 'breakaway' techniques. I left the instruction to the big Swede as he had Juan holding the padded shields and proceeded to demonstrate full force strikes against the pads to the crowd of unsuspecting new recruits (Joe made sure that he put in more striking demonstrations than he would have at any 'normal' session). Juan was used to taking this sort of punishment, so he had no reason to suspect anything at this stage.

As soon as Joe had dispensed with Juan's services (this took two hours,) Billy needed him to assist with the instruction of the breakaway techniques. This involved Juan grabbing Billy with typical close quarter combat grabs and holds and Billy demonstrating to the participants how to escape from and counter against the initial attacks. Billy (also performing more demonstrations than was usual) took great pleasure in escaping with real power and putting just a little more contact than was necessary in to his countering strikes. By the time that the second two hour session had finished I could see that Juan was beginning to wonder what the hell was going on, but he didn't say anything about the punishment that he had been taking through the morning session over the course of the lunch break. In fact he didn't say much at all apart from telling us to "shut the fuck up" as we gave him a lot of grief over Kara and his sleeping habits!

After lunch we had arranged 'Control and Restraint' training for a group of Military Policemen. This involved a whole range of wrist locks, arm locks, strangle holds and arrest techniques. None of which are particularly pleasant to have forced upon you and certainly not after the morning that Juan had just endured.

I led the instruction and had great fun throwing the unfortunate Juan around like a rag doll. Because of the difficult nature of the techniques involved in control and restraint training, the twenty four M.P.'s that were in attendance on that afternoon asked several questions each, and every time that it was feasible, whoever was asked the question, whether it was me, Billy or Joe, Juan was always called over to be demonstrated upon.

For two identical training days the man took this punishment without a single complaint or comment. By the time that we said goodbye to the second day's Military Police group and locked up the training hall for the evening, Juan was black and blue all over. He sat down on the mats trying to stretch his aching and bruised muscles, he looked at me and asked, "What groups have we got in tomorrow Andy?" Before I could answer, Billy had burst out laughing and Joe was diving around on the mats feigning the pain and discomfort that Juan had been subjected to that afternoon – I couldn't help but laugh!

"You nasty fuckin' bastards!" laughed Juan, finally catching on to the all too painful wind-up.

He was never late for an early training session again.

CHAPTER TWENTY

December came around once more and on Christmas Eve I made my obligatory journey to visit my family for the customary celebrations: the usual tedious events of swapping gifts and demonstrations of greed and excess. I continued to feel like the outsider that I had undoubtedly become, but attempted to join in and be part of the family. I spent most of Christmas Day talking to my Grandparents either helping Nan with whatever she was doing in the kitchen or walking 'Towser' the dog with Gramps.

On Boxing Day, I paid a visit to Griff's house with gifts for the two-year-old Rebecca. As I walked up the drive I noticed that there was no Christmas tree in sight and no sign of decorations. I thought that this was strange with a young daughter who would be very excited at this time of year. Thinking that perhaps they had gone away for the holidays, I rang the bell anyway and was surprised when Griff's mother opened the door. I had met the lady on only a couple of occasions but I knew immediately that something was wrong.

Jenny, Griff's wife, came out of the living room looking like shit, her usually beautiful face was contorted with anguish and my heart sank. She ran to me, hugging me and sobbing in to my chest. Trying to comfort and embrace her, I looked enquiringly at Griff's mother.

"Andy, Steve was killed in a car crash on Christmas Eve" she said. I felt feeble and was totally speechless – I just looked at the lady for more information as I held Jenny tighter in my arms now sharing her grief.

"His car was hit by a lorry, a tanker pulling out of the petrol station up the road – oh Andy, he was only half a mile from home!" and with that she joined the embrace and I stood there for some time consoling two ladies that I hardly knew over the death of one of my closest friends.

The following day, I said my farewells and flew back to Samawi, I had decided not to spend New Year in England before I went back, and with the news of Griff's death, there seemed even less to celebrate. Jenny had given me a necklace that Griff had always worn, it had been given to him by his Sensei when he had been a resident student in a Dojo in Japan and Jenny thought that it was appropriate for me to have it. I felt extremely honoured by this gesture.

Arriving back at Nabwana Airport, I collected my luggage and went out to the car park. Throwing my bags in the back of my Land Rover that had been parked in its usual spot while I'd been gone, I began to search through the zip pockets of my rucksack for the keys. I felt a heavy blow on the back of my head and the lights went out.

I stirred in to a semi-conscious state; the first thing that I noticed was the stench, followed rapidly by the pain in my head as I moved slightly. I was lying with the right side of my face pressed down on the filthy floor of a small barn type building, my hands had been taped behind my back – I could feel the adhesive on my arms. It slowly dawned on me that my vision was being hampered, it took me a while to realise that I had been blindfolded with rags and that the cloth had raised enough for me to see out of half of my left eye. My mouth felt as dry as dust and I could feel congealed blood on my face and in my hair.

My mind began to work on fast forward, "It had to be Guerrillas, what a fucking trophy hostage I would make. There was no way that they would set me free no matter what demands were met. If I don't get myself out of here I am fucking dead – no questions asked!"

I tried to roll myself over and the pain in my head fired up again, I fell back on to my face and began to prepare myself for the agony – I had to get up and get myself out of here somehow.

"Come on, think clearly Andy; it's only pain!" I told myself over and over until it became my new mantra.

Through agonizing bolts of pain firing around in my head, I raised my self on to my knees. Nausea washed over me and it was all I could do to keep myself in a kneeling position. I used the mantra again.

"Think clearly; it's only pain!"

Staying in that position for what seemed like hours I began to take full control of my mind again. I had been prepared for this kind of physical discomfort and for fuck's sake I had actually been through worse before.

I got myself to my feet and thanked whoever might be listening that my legs had not been bound too. I walked around in the semi-light that the rag blindfold allowed thinking of how to create an escape opportunity and trying to picture the varying circumstances that may arise.

An engine noise in the distance; a vehicle was approaching. I knew that I would only have one chance to get out of there – one opportunity. If that failed, I would be dead!

The vehicle pulled up outside the building as I put myself down on my knees against the wall farthest from the door.

I could hear two male voices outside – a door slammed and the engine noise disappeared in the distance again. "Could it be that I would only have just the one man to deal with?" I thought fleetingly before correcting that stupid optimism with "your hands are taped behind your back, you can only see out of half an eye, he is probably armed and you have recently had your fucking head caved in – now get a fucking grip and concentrate!"

A chain rattled, a padlock was unlocked and the door began to open, fear rose in the form of nausea once more as I set myself for my 'do or die' attempt.

A man of about the same age as me stood in the doorway; he was wearing the usual camouflage attire of the rebel militia with a rifle slung over his shoulder. He had a bucket in one hand and a stick in the other. He hawked and spat at me and I felt his phlegm hit my neck.

"Do you want the water, or do you want another beating?" he laughed.

I couldn't see what was funny, but I saw my opportunity.

"Please...water!" I said through my genuinely parched throat.

He moved towards me holding out the bucket and raising the stick – but leaving the gun on his back. As the bucket was put on the floor in front of me the stick crashed down on my shoulder and a searing pain shot through me as I began my escape plan. Launching myself forwards by straightening my legs and forcing myself into his stomach I managed to knock him over backwards causing him to fall hard with my bodyweight on top of him. With my hands tied behind my back it was hard to take control but knowing this was my only chance I hit him over and over with my head in to his face. He was tough and kept on struggling for some time but I forced my head down against his face and sank my teeth biting as hard as I could and not letting go until his screams were deafening. I stood up and stamped on his bleeding, damaged face and spitting what was left of the mans nose out of my mouth, with my still bound hands managed to grab the rifle strap and ran out of the door. In the struggle he had done me the unwitting favour of pulling my blindfold completely off, so at least I had full vision again. About a hundred metres away there was a hill lined with trees and vegetation – I made for it as quickly as I could manage.

Once in the trees, I set about ripping the tape from my hands and seeing if I could get some sense of where the hell I was.

In the distance I recognised the town of Cabilo, a town of conflict and a rebel stronghold area. We had been operational on a few missions there but in my present predicament, I didn't think that walking in to a rebel friendly area would be the right thing to do. So, working out my bearings, I headed cross country on foot for around twenty kilometres or so. Finding the road that would take me back to Moyana,

I happened to come upon a gas station where I borrowed the grumpy attendants telephone and arranged to be picked up as soon as possible.

Having been collected by Billy and Joe, I had time to take in the seriousness of the situation and just how lucky I had been. If there had have been men outside, if two men had come in to give me a beating or in any other circumstance, I would not have had a chance. But I survived and got away with nothing more than a sore shoulder and concussion along with a whole lot of mockery from the rest of the team about how I needed to improve my awareness skills to avoid getting bumped on the head!

CHAPTER TWENTY ONE

I was sat in Will Boato's office talking through the experience of the previous few days; I had been checked over by the medics and apart from being prescribed anti-inflammatory tablets and being told not to go banging my head for a week or two , I was quite happy with the diagnosis.

Will was telling me how the Guerrilla militia had stepped up their campaign again over the Christmas period and as well as taking hostages the information gathered by the intelligence unit had put all forces on 'code red' as they were expecting strikes of some form or other at any time.

Sharing lunch with the guys who were about at the time (it was still the holiday season and not everybody was back at the base) we were discussing our plans for celebrating New Year. We had decided that a trip to Nabwana was in order and Jonathan was phoning his parents, who lived on the outskirts of the capitol, to see if they would mind putting five ill-behaved soldiers up for the night.

Joe, Juan, Louis and I were left to wonder if it was the wise thing to do with all the rebel activity that we were being warned about. Joe and I had spoken again to Will Boato and he had given permission on the understanding that we were on the phone to base regularly.

"It's all arranged," said Jonathan as he returned to the table, "I also called my cousin and he has got us tickets to a party!"

We all looked at each other, smiled and shrugged. "I take it we are farken going then?" asked Joe.

"I'm up for it!" Juan said.

"Me too I guess." agreed Louis, they all looked at me.

"Well, you are not leaving me here on my fuckin' own!" I laughed, "Just don't get me banged on the fuckin' head again!"

So, with strict orders for one of us to call Will's office every hour, on the morning of New Year's Eve 1985 the five of us headed off for Nabwana in my Land Rover (I had lost the game of cards to decide who was driving). With Iron Maiden's 'Live After Death" album blasting out of the stereo and the sun blaring down, we were all laughing and looking forward to seeing a New Year in together.

We arrived at Jonathan's parent's house on the edge of town. Jonathan had never talked much about his parents, but on seeing the opulent house and manicured gardens that they owned, one of us had to ask.

"Your Dad is the farken President – eh?" was the subtle Viking approach.

"No, just a lawyer." replied Jonathan with a roll of his eyes, obviously used to the reaction.

"I wouldn't want to pay his farken fees – eh?" laughed Joe.

The whole of Jonathan's family were there to greet us: his parents, younger brother, aunts, uncles and grandparents too. Everybody was great company and they had laid on a huge barbecue and buffet for us before we went out for the night time partying.

After stuffing ourselves on the wonderful array of food for an hour or so, we politely removed ourselves from the family get together, showered, changed and headed into town along with Jonathan's cousin Bruno.

"So," I said, "where are we headed?"

"The Equator Bar!" said Bruno proudly.

I looked at Joe and Jonathan, who both looked as amazed as I was.

"You didn't tell me it was the fucking Equator Bar!" Jonathan said, berating his unwitting cousin.

"Hey...I'm sure it will be fine." I told them, Juan and Louis were looking as confused as poor Bruno. "It's just that the last time we visited the Equator Bar, we had a bit of a tear up, that's all – I'm sure the same guys won't be there!"

So, we all agreed to carry on with the night as planned.

As we entered the Equator Bar there was the familiar atmosphere and the ever-present drunk people flirting, cavorting, fighting and throwing up.

The dance floor was heaving and the usual dodgy DJ was playing the usual crap to the intoxicated crowd's delight. Groups of guys from Nabwana's gang culture stood in small huddles at various points of the venue smoking and dealing dope and generally trying to intimidate the punters.

We made it to the bar through the throbbing crowds and bought a round of drinks each so the bar visits would be minimised and found a patch of wall with a handy shelf to line our drinks up on as we merrily consumed them.

The DJ lived up to his reputation by announcing three in a row from Boney M and Joe was off like a shot, shaking his funky Swedish arse in the middle of the dance floor. The rest of us carried on drinking watching the outlandish gyrating fool strutting his stuff to 'Brown Girl in the Ring' and two other equally iffy tracks.

Several drinks later, all of us were dancing to such classic bands as the Beatles, T Rex, David Bowie and nobody even seemed to mind my Jagger impression this time as the obligatory Rolling Stones tracks were played.

The night went as well as we could have hoped for – we took it in turns to phone in to Will Boato's office and there was no order to return to base – the atmosphere in the club improved as the night went on. As we became more intoxicated, we made friends with the natives and all in all, had a great time seeing in the New Year.

We made it back to Jonathan's parent's house without too much fuss and falling over, before crashing out wherever we landed in the guest rooms.

The morning after arrived all too soon however, and the hangover behind my eyes was the worst that I could remember. At first I thought that something had to be seriously wrong, until I remembered that I was on heavy painkillers and still suffering from concussion. I resorted to the ancient trusted cure of sticking my fingers down my throat and vomiting, swiftly followed by drinking endless glasses of water.

I worried a little less about the state of my health after seeing the appalling condition that the other guys were in. Louis looked like he hadn't slept in months, Juan's eyes had almost completely disappeared in to his head and Joe looked so green skinned that I thought he may have actually changed in to the Incredible Hulk!

Our hosts had laid on another huge buffet for lunch (nobody actually made it out of bed for breakfast) and we ate out of politeness rather than hunger. As soon as good manners allowed, we said thank you to Jonathan's parents and goodbye to all in attendance, chucked our gear in the Land Rover and headed out of the ornate gates.

None of our heads were up to loud rock music, so the stereo stayed off as we travelled along the road that would take us out of the capitol and on to the highway towards Moyana and the base. Although, the moans and groans that so often accompany hangovers were loud enough to hear over the engine noise.

I steered around a large roundabout and took the required exit. As I turned the wheel straight again, the sound of a single gunshot echoed around me and Juan lurched in the passenger seat as a bullet caught him full in the chest, he fell forwards and I immediately feared the worst.

"Joe get up here – stem that fuckin' blood flow now!" I screamed at the Swede who was already moving forwards as I put my foot to the floor to get the vehicle out of range of any more sniper fire and Juan to the nearest hospital.

With Jonathan barking directions at me, Joe trying to keep Juan conscious and me driving like Ayrton Senna on acid, we finally pulled in to the hospital grounds. Four of us carried the blood soaked Juan in to the emergency department and found the nearest available trolley. Jonathan was shouting at the reception desk, Louis was grabbing anybody who vaguely looked like a Doctor and after less than a minute we had three experts shaking their heads in unison and rushing poor Juan in to a treatment room.

For over two hours we waited, drinking coffee that we didn't want, pacing the floors, and asking any passing staff if they could tell us anything about the state of our friend.

Finally the news came that we all feared – Juan had put up a brave fight, but the bullet had caused irreparable damage to his internal organs and he had lost his battle for life.

CHAPTER TWENTY TWO

(February 1986)

With the escalation in troubles from the rebel militia and the recent deaths of some of my closest friends, in times of solitude, I often found myself fighting internal mental battles and had no real desire to celebrate my twenty first Birthday. I would have been happy to share a drink or two on the beach to mark the occasion, Joe and the rest of the unit however, had no intention of letting me avoid a fully blown piss up of a party.

The local government in the town of Moyana had been trying to utilise the facts that the sun always shone in Samawi and that the South Atlantic coastline was indeed magnificently scenic and had begun the slow process of building a tourist industry. One of the first to take advantage of this was a graduate of Oxford University in England. Samawian by birth, he had lived in London for a while working as a stockbroker and making a fair amount of serious money. He was a huge fan of the band Queen, especially the inimitable Freddy Mercury and he went out of his way to model himself upon the outrageous front man.

'Freddy's Bar' had opened in mid January causing a great deal of shock and consternation at the antics of the owner, with his posing and prancing about in imitation of the great performer. He had been a regular at London's more outrageous clubs and dance venues but the vast majority of Moyana's population had never seen the likes of Queen's camp vocalist, and the shockwaves reverberated amongst the devout and pious.

So, with no other choice, I was dragged by the other seven remaining members of our unit to celebrate the twenty first anniversary of my birth at the newly infamous 'Freddy's Bar', overlooking the azure sea with large open sliding doors on the side of the white brick building. Inside there was a two tier dance floor, and a stage suspended on a mezzanine platform in between the two levels, with a huge semi-circular bar at each end of the venue, one on each floor. We arrived very early, late afternoon rather than evening time, as we did not want to waste any valuable drinking time and we walked in to find 'Freddy' on stage, rehearsing one of his routines, which basically involved posturing, posing and prancing around in true 'Mercury' fashion, whilst miming to 'Seven Seas of Rhye'.

'Freddy' like a true professional, finished his routine before rushing to greet us and welcoming us to his establishment. He seemed to be very impressed that an Englishman was in his bar and embraced me like a long lost brother before marching me off (with an amused Viking et al following behind) to introduce me to his daughters whose names were 'Hope' and 'Innocence'. The daughters, who appeared to be around the same age as I was, could have easily been twins. They looked almost identical and played upon this by wearing their hair in the same way to accentuate their cherubic faces and as they shared the management of the bar service for their father, they always wore the same uniforms whilst working.

'Freddy' (if they knew, nobody would tell us his real name) insisted that the first round of drinks were on the house in honour of his "new English friend" and the party got underway in an otherwise empty bar with us all drinking cheap German lager and receiving tips on how to strut like Mr. Mercury. I reciprocated the lesson by trying to show Freddy how to move like Mr Jagger.

We took the liberty of borrowing an acoustic guitar from backstage and we all sat around singing along to whoever was strumming well known, badly played songs into the early evening, with Freddy dropping in and out of the party as he prepared for the expected onslaught of punters.

By the time the first rush of customers appeared at the bar, we had been drinking for a good few hours and had got to know Freddy, Hope and Innocence quite well. Hope lived above the bar in a flat with her husband who was a policeman in Nabwana. Innocence was preparing to emigrate to Los Angeles to marry her American fiancé.

As the room began to fill with people, it was interesting to watch Freddy transform in to the entertainer and 'host with the most' as he made his way onstage and exploded into the first set of his act, welcoming everybody to 'Freddy's Bar' before dancing his way through "Crazy Little Thing Called Love".

At the downstairs bar, which was close to where we sat in an alcove seating area, a group of men were fucking around. The group had looked across to where we were sitting a few minutes before and had felt the need to give us the benefit of a bit of manly eye contact and Neanderthal posturing much to our amusement. They were now pushing each other about whilst dancing along, harmless enough fun, apart from the fact that anybody who was waiting to be served at the bar was getting barged and jostled by their actions. Hope leant across the bar to ask the guys to calm down and was grabbed by the biggest member of the group and had a kiss planted on her lips for her troubles. She took this invasion of her basic human rights with good grace before giving the guy a severe telling off (which we couldn't hear from where we were, but it involved a great deal of finger wagging and pointing towards the exit). This led to the guy (who was easily twice Hope's size) looking very sheepish and obviously apologising to her.

As the night progressed and the empty bottles and glasses mounted up on our table, Joe led the charge on to the dance floor as the DJ (in between sets one and two of Freddy's act) played the now almost legendary 'Iko, Iko' with the eight of us squeezed amongst several hundred other clubbers to copy the big Swede doing the 'Viking Boogie'.

Several equally bad dance tunes later, Freddy took the stage again and Joe and I headed for the bar as the rest of our unit flopped back into the alcove seats. As 'We are the Champions' was belted out on stage, a smiling Hope turned to serve me. As she did so, the big muscled guy who had pulled Hope across the bar earlier that evening swung a huge fist towards my head. I ducked under it and smashed my forearm in to his balls (noticing that Joe was having similar fun with some of my attacker's friends); I slammed a knee hard into the side of the guys head. He was already doubled over from the pain in his groin, so he didn't have that far to drop to the floor. I looked around to see the comical site of each of my friends (all with childish grins on their faces) stood over a floored friend of the big guy who was at my feet moaning alternately about his rapidly swelling temple and the pain in his bollocks. His moans were punctuated with curses questioning my parentage.

Having escorted the failed attackers out of the bar and into the relevant police vehicle or ambulance, we made our humble apologies to Freddy and his daughters. Freddy was not at all angry, "the man who attacked you Andy – did he hit you at all?" he asked

"No, thank fuck!" I replied, "When they are that big, you don't want them hitting you."

"He is from Cobolo." Freddy went on to explain, "He has been here every week since we opened. He told Innocence that he is the Cobolan Heavyweight Boxing Champion!"

I laughed. "I wonder how he's going to explain to his coach that he was crippled by a fucking shrimp of a lightweight in Samawi?" I wondered.

The rest of the night went smoothly and ended back amongst the fruit trees by the pool on camp with a rather magnificent bottle of Talisker single malt whisky that I'd brought back from my last trip home being drained between us.

CHAPTER TWENTY THREE

The following week, I returned to England in order to attend my sister's wedding. I had purposefully made the visit as short as possible, spending most of the time with my Grandparents, but also finding the time to make a brief and emotional visit to Jenny, Griff's widow, and also search through Birmingham's music stores for albums which would enhance my collection.

Returning to Samawi after only a few days, I was greeted at the airport by a stern looking Joe. Sensing his mood, I asked what was wrong.

"The farken Cobolans are over the farken border again," he explained with typical Viking eloquence, "we're farken heading up there again – tonight!"

So two and a half hours after getting off a plane from England, I had travelled back to the base showered, changed, checked and packed my weapons and gear and was sat in a helicopter headed for the northern town of Gabale, with the rest of the Samawian Special Task Force being briefed on our latest mission in the ongoing dispute over the border with the Republic of Cobolo.

A house had been identified in Gabale as the site of a handful of Cobolan nationals that were operating in Samawi. It was thought that the residents of this property had been responsible for several shootings and at least two of the recent bombings in the north of the country. Our task was to enter the house and deal with the occupants before letting the explosive experts in to make safe any potentially explosive nasty stuff!

After another three hours, we had met with the explosives team, been further briefed by the Intelligence Officers who had been operating surveillance on the suspected bombers and had formulated our plan of action.

Dusk had descended upon the area. The house was a small dwelling at the end of a Portuguese style terraced row; the intelligence guys had subtly evacuated the rest of the homes. I was in the road at the front of the property with Joe, Michael and Jonathan. At the rear of the building were Billy, Joseph, Louis and Paul. There were signs of activity in the house and we expected there to be some kind of resistance from the occupying Cobolans. At the given signal we moved in, the familiarity of fear and adrenalin pumping through me as I climbed the trellis on to a small balcony before helping the big Swede to follow me. Michael and Jonathan waited at the front door and window below. We checked watches again to correspond with the plan, then, Michael gave the signal to move in.

Joe forced open the balcony doors and we heard the front door below us crash open as Michael and Jonathan made their entry. As I moved in, a man charged at me with a knife aimed at my guts. I sidestepped his charge slammed my Kalashnikov into his face causing him to sprawl backwards crashing to the floor with his nose and cheekbone smashed. Joe casually picked him up, carried him to the balcony and dropped him to the ground outside. As I looked at him questioningly he said, "He's not farken going anywhere - we'll talk to him later eh?" I shrugged and nodded and moved to go further in to the house when all hell was let loose. The floor shook below us as a deafening explosion reverberated throughout the building; I could hear screams and crashes of breaking glass. A searing pain shot through my left leg and arm as the big Viking and I threw ourselves to the floor, a pointless act as just seconds later with a second explosion the floor crumbled below us and we dropped with it to land in what had been the room below. I was blinded by the dust and grit amid the darkness and confusion. Agony, terror and disorientation washed over me for an unknown time, before my mind fought it's way through to drag me back to the reality of the moment and the fact that I was still in grave danger and my friends were amidst all this destruction too. More than likely they were in worse condition than I was, probably even dead. I had to get to them. Once again I repeated to my self, "It's only pain. It's only pain!" as I tried to ignore the agony shooting through the left side of my body and struggled to undo my backpack to find my water bottle and splash my eyes to wash the shit and dust away. As I did so, I realised the root of the problem. I noticed what had been impeding my hand movements in the blind grapple with my backpacks buckles. A large splinter of glass had entered in to the palm of my left hand and had embedded itself. As I extracted it I realised it was around three inches long and must have reached well into my wrist. Fearing what I might see, I looked down at my leg; an even larger shard had found its way in to my knee. Removing the offending objects as quickly as I could, I cleaned the wounds and began to look around in the devastation for my friends. Joe was closest to me; just his head and shoulders were visible below the loose rubble that had landed on top of him. I checked his neck for a pulse and should not have been surprised to find a strong one. I splashed water onto his face as I said, "come on wake up you fuckin' great turnip!" His eyes opened slowly, "you took your farken time!" he said.

After establishing that the almost un-human Viking had no more than cuts, bruises and a sore head, I helped him from beneath the rubble and he joined me in search of the others. We found Billy with his tibia sticking out of his shin, grinning at us from his position propped up against what was left of a wall. With blood pouring from a gash in his forehead he said, "Any one for long jump – you might have a chance at the moment!" I answered him with all the grace I could muster. "Shut the fuck up!" I said as I began to dress his wounds using my field pack, "there'll be some real medics here soon my friend!" I added. Joe turned to carry on searching,

"Louis is dead." Billy called out as I pressed the mocked up splint too hard on to his broken leg. He was pointing to his left where shreds of the Samawian uniform were visible on the edge of a piece of corrugated steel laying upon the rubble. Joe moved closer and tentatively began to lift the metal. I watched with Billy as the Swede peered under – he immediately dropped the steel and vomited furiously with the sight of what lay under there.

"Fark! Fark! Fark!" he shouted through the retching, "it took his farken head off – Fark!"

The realisation of more of our team not making it through the blasts hit me, and I left Billy to go in search of the others. Michael was okay; he had been knocked unconscious by flying debris. He had cracked ribs and a broken clavicle along with the cuts and bruises, but he was alive. Joseph had been trapped beneath a falling wall which had broken both of his legs. He was 'lucky' that they had not been totally crushed.

Jonathan was still alive when I found him too, but despite my best efforts and those of Joe to apply pressure and care to his stomach wounds (thinking that emergency aid would be arriving any moment), the huge piece of glass that had embedded in his guts had caused too many internal injuries and he died as I begged him to hold on to life. We never found Paul's body, he had been very close to the initial blast and the bomb had literally blown him to bits. Five Cobolans had also met the same fate (through choice) in that 'suicide bombing'. The whole mission had been a complete fuck up!

After what seemed like an age, a small convoy of two ambulances, the explosives team's vehicles, and the Intelligence Commander's car arrived at the devastated house.

I was at the front of the site trying to make Michael more comfortable – the more time I had had to think about the whole mission while searching and treating those of my friends which had survived, the angrier I became.

As the medics ran towards me I directed them to the survivors, pointing out that there was also a Cobolan with a smashed face and a broken leg in the front yard, who Intelligence would no doubt want to talk to. The Explosives

Chief and Intelligence Commander followed behind walking towards me.

"How far fuckin' back were you?" I demanded, "where was the fuckin' intelligence in that?"

"Sorry!" said the Commander.

"Come with me!" I pulled at his sleeve and led him behind the only part of the wall that was still standing upright. As we reached a dark spot where I was certain that nobody could see us, I turned and head butted him with all the anger of the night behind the blow. "Cunt!" I told him as he hit the ground.

There were plenty of repercussions and enquiries over that dreadful event, not least of which was the official investigation by the Intelligence Unit into their Commander's mysterious injury. Despite their insistence over my guilt and demands to have 'the foreigner' drummed out of Samawi, none of the statements given by those who had been present related to the Commander's version of the assault. In fact I had been so busy dressing wounds and caring for everybody else in my unit that I was heralded a hero of the mission and awarded with a medal by the Samawian President. It did not make up for the loss of three more of my closest friends.

Over the course of the following month or so of healing, Billy, Michael and Joseph found great amusement in the fact that I was suffering more from the pain of tendon and nerve damage caused by the glass shards than they were from their broken bones. For a good while I had been on a daily dose of antibiotics and anti-inflammatory tablets that would have been enough to calm an angry bull elephant and in order to take my mind off the discomfort. I had re-immersed myself in the familiarity of managing the instruction in the combat training hall alongside Joe, who had already healed from his insignificant injuries.

With the deaths of Jonathan, Paul and Louis still distressing, and Benni's and Juan's deaths still relatively fresh in our minds, we often got together over the ensuing weeks to talk and help each other through the ubiquitous emotional rollercoaster. One evening sat under the fruit trees by the pool, the five of us were trying to make sense of that catastrophic night in Gabale. The conversation lulled as we began to run out of emotional energy and, as all fell silent, Joe passed the ever-present battered old acoustic guitar to me. I started to gently strum and sing Bob Dylan's 'Blowing in the Wind', with the tears rolling down my cheeks and the words catching in my throat, the true brilliance and significance of the lyrics actually dawned on me for the very first time.

CHAPTER TWENTY FOUR

As the regular forces began to take more control of the disputed border lands with Cobolo and the internal struggle with the rebel militia began to wane, the final remaining five original members of the Samawian Special Task Force began to initialise a selection and training process for the development and advancement of a new team. Out of those of us remaining, Billy, Michael and Joseph were all in their mid to late thirties and had all taken more than their fair share of punishment. That only left Joe and myself, both of us were 'officially' only guests and there were underlying rumblings in the top brass that we should be taking a less active role!

So with a little re-organisation and many hours of discussions with Will Boato and other senior figures, we began to develop a bigger better version of the Samawian Special Task Force, with a designated barracks within the base at Moyana. There had been twelve of us in the original unit – the five of us that had survived now had a new remit. We were to help train and develop a new fighting force of one hundred outstanding soldiers (selected by Will Boato) who would be capable of taking over from ourselves with an enhanced methodology. This new outlook gave us all a fresh impetus and we set about our new duties with renewed vigour and enthusiasm.

During their recovery period, Michael and Joseph had become drawn towards Christianity. Whether it was down to the near death experience of that fucked up mission or maybe the frequent visits from the military preacher, Christophe, who had become a friend to us all in his visits to the ward during our communal convalescence. Billy was as cynical as Joe and I were about religion in general, but Michael and Joseph became more interested in the Christian beliefs of Christophe the Priest and his biblical tales and viewpoints.

My true opinion on the subject of religion of any kind was that if there was a divine being of any form controlling the matters of the world, he or she must have a fucking sick sense of humour to allow all the violence, hatred and bloodshed to continue.

On the first of our 'long weekend off' excursions after the 'broken boned three' were released from hospital, we met up as usual at Billy's quarters in the base grounds to set off for a planned peaceful few days in Calo. As Michael and Joseph arrived together, they told us that they had invited Christophe the Priest along for the trip.

So, after rearranging the mode of transport (swapping my Land Rover for a larger long wheel base version), we made our way to the chapel in the centre of Moyana where Christophe lived and worked. We arrived at his flat; Michael jumped out of the back with a big smile on his face and went to knock the door to find out if the priest was ready to go. He returned a few minutes later with a puzzled expression and explained that there had been no answer. We decided to go and see if he was waiting at the chapel which was just a few hundred metres walk along an alleyway from where we were parked. Billy volunteered to mind the vehicle.

We approached the small church, which looked to me as though somebody had picked it out of a village setting in rural Britain and dumped it undamaged to leave it nestling amongst the winding alleys and houses in the centre of this small African coastal town.

As we entered the building we could hear raised voices coming from the opposite end. We were in a house of worship and had no reason to suspect any trouble of any kind, but Joe and I immediately took to opposite sides of the aisle and, with Michael and Joseph following behind, worked our way towards the heated conversation. In a small room to the right of the pulpit, Christophe was surrounded by four guys (they did not give the appearance of being regular members of his congregation). It was obvious that the Priest was trying to stay calm, telling them that he was unable to meet with the gang's demands. The four men were becoming agitated and it was clear that Christophe was losing control of the situation. Joe signalled that he and Joseph would move in to the room and that I should stay put with Michael as back up.

As one of the gang grabbed the Priest by his collars, Joseph stepped in to the doorway. "Good morning Father – is there a problem here?" he asked as the big Swede stepped up behind him.

"We have no problem with you Mr Soldier," answered one of the men, "so go while you can eh?"

"This is a house of God." continued Joseph ignoring the threat, "I will go when I know that the Priest is safe and well – I think that it is you who should leave eh?" With this, two of the gang members moved to attack Joseph and the Swede while the other two began to rough Christophe up and demand money from the priest. Michael and I moved in to dissuade them from their actions. Michael threw himself forwards to land a flying elbow into the nose of the man holding Christophe. As I moved forwards, the last gang member pulled a knife from a sheath on his belt and raised his arm as if to stab the Priest. I grabbed the limb just as he began the arc of the attack and managed to lock his arm and turn it behind him, kicking hard in to the back of his knee I dropped the man to the floor dropping him on to his own blade. As he landed I stamped hard on to his sternum to make sure that he didn't get any ideas about getting up again for a while.

The other three members of the group had been similarly taken care of and

Christophe began to explain that the men had been calling each week since he had taken his position at the Chapel, demanding money to 'not damage the building or its contents!'

After trussing them up with whatever we could lay our hands on (bootlaces, belts and sticky tape) Joe, Joseph and I marched the complaining group down the road to the local police station where we knew a few officers who would be quite prepared to make the gang's life a misery in order to deter them from threatening Holy Men or restarting any protection rackets in the town.

Returning to the vehicle we had to wake Billy from a deep slumber; he had slept in the Land Rover through the entire incident. After the sleeping beauty had dried himself off from the canteens of water that a certain Viking and long haired Englishman had tipped over him , we were heading south on our way to Calo and a relaxing weekend on the white sands with a happy and relieved Christophe on board.

The journey there was hilarious as we introduced the relatively naive Priest to the experience of Iron Maiden's 'Number of the Beast' and similar such tracks. We continued to expose him to the talents of Steve Harris, Bruce Dickinson and company for the next few days. As the heavy rock tunes blasted from the cassette player, we messed around on the beach playing football and volley ball during the days and resting around a camp fire as dusk fell and we drank and talked in to the night.

By the time we returned to Moyana on the Monday evening Christophe was seen as a true friend (even though Billy, Joe and I remained totally agnostic) and the holy man had started to recognise a good rock track when he heard one too!

CHAPTER TWENTY FIVE

Being in a position of authority and responsibility at the Nation's foremost military base came with a large number of both plus and minus points; an example of a dubious plus point was the fact that we had a "mutually beneficial" arrangement with the Samawian Presidential Offices. This agreement meant that we would train appointed guards in a multitude of combat skills and in return (if extra guards were needed) we would get roped into the mundane world of body guarding politicians, and various VIPs.

I had never been impressed with politics or politicians. I did not see famous people as being superior to the less well-known and therefore did not recognise 'celebrity' as a status (making the occasional hypocritical exception for rock guitar and vocal heroes.) Consequently, I was never the first to volunteer for close quarter protection work when it came along. Joe had (probably unsurprisingly) much the same opinion as I had and because of that fact, we were both extremely down hearted when we were told that we had been assigned to the unit of officers protecting the Samawian President during the event of a conference which involved a multitude of foreign dignitaries in Nabwana.

We had been on seven such jobs together before, usually for 'second string' politicians who were full of self-importance and some of the most arrogant people that I have ever had the misfortune to meet. Three of the jobs however had been for so called 'stars'. One of which was a world famous entertainer who had been contracted by the government to perform at the National football stadium. Our job had been to protect him as he was taken on a tour of Samawi (a pointless task as ninety nine percent of the population would not have recognised him if he had slapped them with a wet fish and given his name). The man had been so used to having an entourage of sycophants around him and so wrapped up in his persona that he did not speak other than to make demands. That was unless he was sure that a camera was pointing at him; he seemed to have a sixth sense which told him when he was in the proximity of an uncapped lens, in which case his whole demeanour changed and he suddenly became the smiling 'star' that everybody loved once more.

Another such duty had been to protect a superstar movie actor and director who was visiting Samawi to search for possible locations to use for his next film. Considering he was known as one of Hollywood's leading lights, from what we had seen, he was not exactly Mr Personality! He had again been full of ego and self-importance and had talked down to us for the whole time that we were with him. He would also make a point of arguing with us when we advised him on measures to assure his safety, and he treated his employees like something that he had stepped in. I had been amazed that he didn't need a bodyguard to protect him from his staff let alone the public!

The one exception to the rule of miserable egotistical people in need of protection had been an Australian comedy performer who we had been assigned to guard. He had been extremely friendly and down to earth, not only by allowing us to advise and guide him when necessary, but also inviting us to after show parties and treating us like friends when we arrived at the functions armed with uncomfortable grins.

The task of protecting the President and his government involved the International Conference, a Gala Ball for a thousand VIPs and an International Football match involving the Samawian national team. The risk of threat to the leading politicians had heightened since the troubles with the Republic of Cobolo and the rebel militia had made an ongoing target of Samawi's Government Officials.

At the pre-emptory briefing with the leading officers from Samawi's Special Police and Army Units, Joe and I were assigned to protect a man that we had met on a number of occasions before. His name was John Kalebo and he was the Prime Minister of Samawi, a charismatic man with an intense manner without being abrupt or discourteous. He was just as much a target as the President as it had been Mr Kalebo who had been responsible for several of the policies that had led to the quelling of guerrilla uprisings and indeed the border dispute with Cobolo.

Waking in a twin room in the most luxurious hotel in Nabwana on the morning of the International Conference, I was shaken into a state of realism by the sound of a Viking singing, farting and making coffee all at the same time; I looked at the clock, it was 5.00am. "One day you will make somebody a lovely fucking wife – d'you know that!" I told him.

"Fark you!" he replied smiling, "do you want a coffee?"

Drinking the offered coffee, we discussed the seriousness of the day's responsibility and we were dragged back in to a more professional mode as we donned formal suits and wandered down the plush corridors of the hotel to escort the Prime Minister to breakfast in the dining room.

"Why the fuck can't he have room service? That way, we could have a lie in 'til 6.00am at least!" I whispered sarcastically as we approached the P.M.'s suite.

"He has to get his face in front of all the farken cameras!" observed the equally cynical Swede.

We switched from being our naturally mocking and jokey selves to be fully alert and professional guards as we joined with the other assigned officers and observed the surroundings, atmosphere and happenings in the vicinity of our designated charges.

Breakfast went without any more excitement than a waiter dropping a jug of milk and an over exuberant officer pulling his gun on the poor kid as the crash of glass hitting the floor jangled his nerves.

A whole fleet of black limousines, Rolls Royces and Bentleys, all with highly trained police drivers, lined the street waiting for the signal that there designated politician was ready to be driven to the Conference at Samawi's Parliament Halls. There were all shapes and colours of ensigns on the front and rear of the vehicles; familiar flags for the Ambassadors of the U.S.A., Australia, U.K., France and other leading European nations, along with a vast assortment of ones that I did not recognise from obscure parts of Africa and the Middle East.

As an officer signalled for our Bentley to approach, I stepped forward onto the walkway and into the flashing frenzy of photographers and yelling journalists. With John Kalebo on my right – Joe was on his other side - we made it half way across the pavement towards the open car door when a man barged through the chain of police men to my left and ran straight towards us. His hands were empty but his mouth was on fast forward and he was screaming in a crazed kind of hatred at Mr Kalebo. As had been planned, Joe grabbed the Prime Minister and rushed him (well, more sort of hurled him) in to the waiting car as I moved to deal with the attack. The crazed man raced straight in to my foot, which was aimed at his knee, and as he fell, an alert policeman, swiftly followed by two others dived on him to restrain and check for any "horrible stuff" such as explosives.

As I turned to return to the care of John Kalebo another man had taken advantage of the confusion and burst forwards with a revolver held high and aimed towards the Prime Minister's car. Without any hesitation I did what I had often doubted I would be able to do in order to protect a politician, I launched myself full force at the gunman hitting him in the ribcage underneath his weapon arm and causing him to fire up in to the sky, as we were falling my full attention switched to controlling the hand with the gun in it as I had to make certain that the killing machine was not pointing at me. I was pleasantly surprised and very fucking relieved to hear the metallic sound of gun hitting concrete some way from us as we hit the ground. I wrapped the guy up in to a stranglehold, turned and pinned him to the floor as yet more policemen appeared on the scene to take him away.

Joe had ordered John Kalebo's driver to "farken go!" as the gunman had moved in, so I grabbed a ride with another Limo to the Conference.

Radical events such as the attempted assassination of the Samawian Prime Minister had almost become everyday stuff to us since taking the decision to stay on in Samawi. This was never more obvious than when I walked in to the Parliament Halls to the Conference venue and nothing was said. I walked over to the big Swede who just nodded, clasped my hand in greeting and asked, "you okay?" I nodded and he went on to brief me on the things that I'd missed and we went on with watching the most dull and uninteresting conference in the history of the world.

The evening saw the gathering of politicians move back to the hotel and the extremely ornate ballroom was the setting for the Gala Ball. A supposedly famous British orchestra (that this Brit had never heard of) had been flown in especially for the occasion to play tunes for the VIPs to dance along to. The evening went without any further adventure other than a Viking and a scrawny Englishman craftily ogling the more attractive female guests by strategically manoeuvring our observation work to a more favourable advantage point.

The next morning saw the Prime Minister meet with the President and the U.S. Ambassador as we waited outside a secure room at the Presidential palace.

The afternoon was the International Football match and we were keen to get the Prime Minister seated in his VIP box seat. We sat in the row behind him; Joe two seats to his right and I was seated to his left. The ground was very heavily policed and there was no sign of any trouble at all. Samawi won the match by a single goal to nil in a very dull game that would not have looked out of place in the English lower leagues – lots of passion but very little skill!

At the end of the day, after returning him safely to his veritable fortress of a residence in the centre of Nabwana, John Kalebo turned to me, shook my hand and said, "I never had chance yesterday – I want to say thank you for what you did!"

CHAPTER TWENTY SIX

(September 1986)

Will Boato had called us into his office and had thrown two fat envelopes onto his desk. "Take one each," he ordered, "this is the calculated pay that is due to you for the outstanding service you have given to the Samawian Military."

I glanced at Joe; he was stood staring at the white envelopes on the highly polished wooden desk. I suddenly realised that I had been holding my breath since the envelopes had hit the desk and blew out heavily through my lips as I shrugged my shoulders and moved forwards to take one envelope and passed the other to the stationary Swede. I opened the package with the fumbling fingers of a seven year old at Christmas and my jaw dropped at the sight of more cash than I had ever seen, let alone had for myself.

We had spent the whole of our time in Samawi without a fixed rate of pay; the arrangement had never been an official one – we had been given free rooms, meals, vehicles and anything else that we required and in addition to that, we had only to ask if we needed funds for travelling home, holidays or just required extra spending money. Not the kind of employment agreement that the average English company would offer; I had neither thought nor cared about pensions or savings at the time of the offer and had shrugged the subject off when it had been raised by my family. But it appeared that the Samawian Military had seen fit to save some funds for me and those funds were now safely buttoned in to the pocket of my combat pants.

The next morning Iron Maiden's "The Trooper" was blasting from the stereo of my open topped Land Rover; the brilliant track describing the terrible massacre of the Light Brigade. With a Viking in the passenger seat, the two of us were singing at the top of our voices trying desperately to harmonise with the backing vocals as we made our charge in to Nabwana.

We were heading in to the capitol city to visit the sprawling markets and spend some of the cash that had been handed to us by Will Boato.

We parked up outside a hotel that we had visited many times previously and went in to the Cafeteria for a coffee and a syrupy pecan nut pastry before heading in to the madding crowds of the bustling and boisterous market quarters.

On market days, the centre of Nabwana was literally split into four separate areas, each with a huge market of its own. The areas appeared to be split not only according to the varying goods that the stalls were selling, but also by the faiths and ethnicity of the stallholders themselves. This led to a fascinating atmosphere within the various quarters and frequent melees amongst stallholders as differing beliefs and cultures clashed.

We made our way from the hotel to the deafening rows of food stalls, this area included traders selling fruits, nuts, seeds and vegetables interspersed with vendors of live chickens, goats and sheep those of which lucky creatures were safely categorised as food for either their usefulness in providing eggs and milk. The unlucky ones were purchased by people with the intention of slaughtering them when they got home and using them as meat.

Having tried to ignore the livestock, we bought a bag of mixed dried fruit to eat as we wandered the market and headed off to a string of stalls that sold 'western' clothing. This was basically a couple of guys from Samawi that had family in the U.S.A. and had an arrangement with them to send frequent batches of Levi jeans and other well known brands of clothing to Nabwana for them to sell for a huge profit. I succumbed to temptation and treated myself to a pair of jeans and a T-shirt.

We stopped for a cold beer at a tavern with tables outside and we sat and watched the multitudes pass and made mocking remarks at the expense of the bizarre and wonderful people amongst the crowds.

With the cool drink inside us, we walked on towards the other side of the centre in order to find a music stall that we had visited many times previously on the off chance that the stall holder would have a decent rock cassette amongst his merchandise.

As we moved through the crowds, a woman caught my arm and asked me to buy from her basket of confectionary. I smiled and declined her offer as I had been caught out by the delicious looking sweets before – they were incredibly sour and far too tangy for my taste.

We moved down a walkway that led to the music store and the crowds started to thin out as we walked away from the more popular areas. I turned to a stall selling hats and reached to try on a cowboy hat that failed miserably at its intended role of making me look like Clint Eastwood in the spaghetti westerns. As I replaced the hat on its hook with the big Swede whispering piss-taking remarks about longhaired gunslingers down my ear, the hum of people was shattered by the crack of gunfire and I instinctively dived to the ground using the hat stall as cover. Silence descended for a few seconds as I lay on the ground, noticing that blood was splattered over my shirt I quickly looked behind me and I froze at the sight of Joe lying motionless on his stomach in the dirt at the edge of the walkway just centimetres from me.

I dived towards him and knew immediately that he was dead. The snipers bullet had hit him clean in the side of his head and there was no recognisable feature left. The hum of the crowd rose again after a few more seconds of the gunshot not being repeated and the locals began to realise that some other poor bastard had been the target.

I fell apart – this had not been a mission, this had been a day of relaxation and fun! We had not been on duty; we were fucking shopping! This had been the most relaxed that either of us had been for the last five years and now Joe was fucking dead, his head blown apart, lying in a pool of blood in the dirt of Nabwana's market!

I knelt by the body of the man who had been like the brother I never had to me, and, as the blood soaked into my clothes, the emotions poured out of me in huge howls and wails, shouts and roars.

The tears and angst were not purely for Joe, the grief for all the other lost friends came out too, but the loss of my closest companion had tipped me over the edge. None of the public came close as I let the emotions wash over me. If the sniper was still there he would have had a sitting duck as a target – the thought actually occurred to me through the grief - I did not care!

Eventually the police arrived closely followed by an army unit, I was totally numb during the journey back to the base in Moyana and was left to my own devices to clean up and grieve in my room until Will Boato appeared at my door with a look of huge empathy and concern on his face and an equally compassionate Billy, Michael and Joseph with him. "This is no time to be on your own Andy." Will told me.

"We should remember him together – eh?" Billy said with a sorrowful smile.

I looked at the faces of my few remaining friends, each of them as sincere as anything that I had ever had the privilege of being party to.

Without saying a word I reached in to the cupboard by my door, grabbed the last remaining bottle of single malt whisky and walked in silence to the beach with the only people left who understood what I was going through.

CHAPTER TWENTY SEVEN

(December 1986)

Heathrow Airport was packed full of people armed with bags full of presents for loved ones at Christmas (which was only two days away.)

I had said my long drawn out goodbyes to Billy, Michael, Joseph and Will Boato, after battling mentally with myself for a couple of months, before finally admitting that I had to leave Samawi to keep things together.

Things at the base in Moyana had been pretty rough after Joe had died. We had always been a double act, almost permanently together. My temper had been operating on an incredibly short fuse and I had snapped on several occasions. I had been talking to Army psychologists and other so called experts for weeks on end, I had spent a great deal of time with Will Boato but I had not reacted at all well to the death of the big Swede. After all the deaths of my close friends and colleagues, his death had been the proverbial straw that broke the camels back.

I had made up my mind to leave when I had been sitting drinking with Billy and Michael at the pool by the fruit trees one evening. Billy had made a typically jovial comment about my nasty temper when I suddenly flew at him with my fist raised ready to strike. I stopped myself just in time with Billy thankfully being as understanding and forgiving as always. I still knew that I had to leave.

I had no idea what I was going to do in England – so I was sat in the café at the airport, with none of my family aware that I was back in the U.K. I was trying to work out how I could make my life bearable. I toyed with ideas of just grabbing a train to Cumbria or the North of Scotland and trying to find employment in the mountains somehow. I thought of taking a further flight to Italy to try and find some work in the tourist trade in the Dolomites – all flights of fancy – but all more attractive than returning to my parents house.

However much I thought of alternatives, as evening fell in Birmingham I found myself knocking on the door to my parents house and having to explain to an incredulous Mother and Father that I was home to stay (not just for Christmas). There was an awful amount of tut-tutting and head shaking, sighing and huffing, none of which led me to feel welcome or helped me to believe that I should not have gone with the 'turning in to a mountain guide' option. Thankfully my Dad had already stocked up on booze for the holidays, so I was able to engross myself with the safe activity of getting inebriated as my parents doled out the phrase "I told you so!" in lots of fairly predictable but different ways.

The following morning, with a thumping hangover, I unpacked my bags and sorted through my belongings – tears filled my eyes as I looked through the photographs of my five years in Samawi. The familiar faces and places – the lost friends happily smiling out from the glossy paper. I decided that perhaps my Dad had been right all along; perhaps I never should have gone to Africa. I had been through all that hate, fear and violence and had ended up back at home with nothing to show for it other than a few blemishes and marks on the outside and a myriad of scars on the inside. After another failed attempt at a conversation with my parents, "Andy – you are home now, forget about Africa and get on with your life!" being the closest thing to empathy that they had to offer, I went for a walk on that cold Birmingham Christmas Eve.

With the full intension of going straight to visit with my Grandparents, an impulse took me into a Barbers shop – for five years Will Boato, Joe and just about everybody else in the Samawian Army had been telling me to get a haircut; I always knew that I needed to cut it, but refused anyway – back in the U.K. I knew that I didn't need to, so I had the whole lot taken off!

Shocked at myself for taking the drastic step of 'close-cropping' the locks, I dispensed with the idea of inflicting my sombre mood on Nan and Gramps at Christmas Eve. Instead, I took a slow walk back via the local music store where I purchased the latest Iron Maiden release "Somewhere in Time". Returning home, I gathered the items that I'd earlier left sorted on my bed. Carrying the bundle out in to the garden, I dropped them on the ground at the side of my Mum's greenhouse. I then fetched the cassette player from my room and putting the brand new tape in to play, I wandered back up the garden and in to my Dad's workshop looking for two more items. On finding them, I walked along the path and began pouring petrol from the can I had just collected on to the pile of photographs, army fatigues and other African memories. As Bruce Dickinson appropriately sang of "Wasted Years…" the memories raced through my mind, grief tore through my heart and tears streamed from my eyes.

Standing in a back garden in Birmingham on a cold Christmas Eve, I told myself once more "It's only pain…"

ABOUT THE AUTHOR

Andy Hopwood is the Founder and Chief Instructor of the BFFA (British Free Fighting Academy) and is widely recognised as being one of the leading authorities on self protection and self defence.

Andy has twice been inducted in to the martial arts world's prestigious 'Combat Hall of Fame'.

He has made several instructional DVD's on effective street self defence and instructs seminars to the corporate market, schools and to the general public worldwide.

Printed in the United Kingdom
by Lightning Source UK Ltd.
115985UKS00001B/61-75